STUCK
IN THE SICK ROLE

How Illness Becomes an Identity

by

MELISSA STENNETT DEUTER, MD

Copyright

The information in this book is meant to offer advice and share my personal experience with parents. This book is not intended as a substitute for any medical advice or professional advice about any specific experience or situation related to children. As each family situation is different, parents should seek the advice of their own physician or medical professional.

Privacy Disclaimer:

If you are connected with my clinical practice as a patient or parent, you may read case examples in these pages and wonder, "Is this case about me?" The answer is emphatically No! I have changed the names and details in every case to make each one unrecognizable from real patients and their families. However, problems with getting STUCK in the sick role have become so pervasive that altering such details invariably makes the story begin to sound like a dozen other real people.
I respect your privacy too much to discuss your personal struggles here without explicit permission. If we didn't talk about your story being in this book, it isn't you.

AUTHOR'S NOTE
STUCK, NOT SICK

I work in Urgent Care. Psychiatric Urgent Care. Sigma Mental Health Urgent Care came to life in 2015. The clinic is innovative, a major shift from how outpatient psychiatry has been practiced for decades, and a shift in the right direction: addressing shortage areas in the field and handling many problems before true crisis sets in. Before I owned an urgent psychiatric clinic, I worked solely as an outpatient psychiatrist for more than a decade, over time in the niche of emerging adult mental health. This became my area of expertise because I liked working with teens and young adult patients, while many of my colleagues seemed to shy away from them. In Urgent Care, emerging adults are still a mainstay of the people coming in. Young people, lost and in crisis (or pseudo-crisis), represent the majority of folks who need answers. "What's wrong with me?" "Is this normal?" "Is my problem a mental disorder?" "If a mental disorder, what is it called, and how can it be treated?"

I have been trying throughout my work with young people to educate families about the difference between "symptoms" like depression and anxiety, and "illnesses" such as Major Depression and Panic Disorder. I have also tried to focus on stage of life development when relevant, and taken care not to label young people experiencing

iv ◄ Stuck in the Sick Role

new symptoms with serious, life-long disorders. Now I am teaching members of my clinical team to approach our patients from the same perspective. I encourage them to view patients in their psychosocial context, stage of life, and consider their working skill set.

Statistically, teens and young adults are at risk for the start of many mental illnesses. Sometimes illnesses begin during those vital years, but sometimes the distress of so much growth and change gets mistaken for illness where there is none. Or mild, transient illness is misunderstood as long-lasting disease, when that is not necessarily so. Often the "disability" for an emerging adult having a crisis outpaces the amount of actual *disease*. People are knocked out of commission by mild problems, especially if the problems hit before adulthood is comfortably achieved. When a wobbly young adult is trying to go out on her own in life for the first time, it may only take a small blow to knock her down.

Sorting out serious illness from not-serious illness can be hard for families. Parents of young adults become trapped with their kids failing to launch, often uncertain whether the adult kids are "sick" or just "stuck." Sometimes adult kids stagnating at home are either stuck or sick, or they are both stuck and sick at the same time.

Meanwhile, psychiatry doesn't really address these questions effectively. Doctors diagnose and treat disease with our prescription pads and operating rooms as the primary tools. The doctor makes a diagnosis and prescribes a treatment for a young adult in crisis without thinking much about the consequences of diagnosis and treatment on the patient's development into adulthood. Virtually everyone seeking consultation with the doctor is offered disease diagnosis and treatment, not guidance or reassurance. No one is sent away with a clean bill of health. Families don't get the answers they seek. They get prescriptions for pills and interventions.

I started out with the standard approach, the one my professional training had offered me. I applied the checklists, diagnosed the psychiatric syndromes, and wrote the requisite prescriptions. And then I watched as my patients stayed stuck in disability long after their psychiatric symptoms had abated. I developed a healthy skepticism, and began creating solutions for families one at a time. I did this by listening, and learning from the patients and their families what worked and what didn't.

Over time, I became the go-to psychiatrist for teens, young adults, and failure to launch situations in my community. My advice is always the same, and it's simple: disease is not the same as disability. Young adults need skills. Parents have to hold their kids accountable, not rescue them. We cannot control other adults, even when those adults are our children. And the bottom line is that parents have to push their kids to take on adulthood as much as possible, and then let them go so they can fly on their own.

After years of one-on-one explanations and guidance for families affected, I finally vowed to get the word out to more than the families who visit my clinics. If you are a family with a stuck person, I hope this book provides you with an understanding of the causes of getting stuck, and a blueprint for change.

TABLE OF CONTENTS

PART 3

INTRODUCTION

Michael's parents wore desperate expressions as they dragged him to the mental health urgent care clinic for a second opinion. Michael had "no life;" he was a lump under the covers upstairs. When he first put school and work on hold to deal with his crisis, Michael's parents said, "Yes, of course. If you're having trouble, let's bring you home for a while. Take all the time you need." They contacted a psychotherapist and psychiatric physician. He would go to regular appointments with the therapist and take medication prescribed by the psychiatric specialist, and his parents told him he would bounce back to his former self, even if it took a few months.

Once home, he only appeared capable of managing the minimum each day. Michael went off to mental health appointments, stopped by the pharmacy to pick up prescriptions, and then he was back home in bed without a word to anyone in the house. He stayed like that for weeks. Then there was a glimmer of hope during weeks six through ten. Family dinners and conversations seemed to signal a return to normalcy and point to a future recovery. His parents were hopeful that a few weeks for recovery had provided the much-needed opportunity for healing, and he was getting better. He was improving, just as they had pictured he would. They saw smiles and laughter. But then Michael gradually slipped back. He fell back into the pattern of appointments and silence and then putting his head under the covers in bed. The laughter and smiles decreased and disappeared. His parents tried not to worry. They decided recovery might take a little bit longer. They waited patiently at first.

Days, weeks, and months passed without any additional signs of improvement and the parents' desperation began to build. Michael was getting treatment, but he wasn't improving. His parents put calls in to his treatment providers to express their concerns, but no one called them back. Nothing got better in the months that followed, not even in a small way. When they flipped their calendar and realized it marked a full year that Michael had been hiding up in his room with no indication that he would be returning to college (or going out to start on any other path to begin his adult life) in the foreseeable future, that was when the panic hit them. *Was his depression so severe that a year of treatment hadn't touched it? Did the doctor and therapist even know the whole story? Was it normal to shut the parents, who were paying the medical bills, out of the process? Was he on the wrong meds? Did he need therapy every day instead of once or twice a week? What were they missing?*

When Michael stepped into the sick role with depression, the plan had seemed realistic enough: take a six month break to get intensive treatment, return to his former state of good health, and then go back to school, refreshed and ready. His obvious strengths would presumably carry him through it. An A student in a prestigious pre-med program with a part-time job as a scribe in an orthopedic clinic, Michael had made college look easy. In fact, it was difficult for his parents to believe him when he initially confessed he had been seeing a counselor at school for several months for depression. He was still making great grades, still working, still calling home on weekends telling stories about rowdy roommates and competitive pre-med peers. From the outside, there had been no signs of trouble. But Michael had broken down to his parents on one of their weekly calls and pled for their help. He asked to step back from responsibilities to get himself better. The counselor at the student health clinic on campus told Michael she was worried and advised him to involve his family. She had suggested taking the rest of the semester off, returning home, and get treatment for while before returning to campus.

He was advised he should start taking medication and see a psychotherapist in his hometown during his months away. This would help him get well, and then he would come back to school. He was in the middle of second semester of third year when the distress call came, and as a seasoned student he was expected to get back on course when he felt ready. Michael's parents had spoken with the counselor from the student clinic over the phone. She had said Michael was a good scholar and a likable young man. The counselor was hopeful that his improvement would be straightforward. She told them she felt certain some supportive time with his family away from the pressures of school would expedite his recovery from depression.

Michael's mom and dad had taken comfort in the recommendation from an experienced professional. It would be fine. They believed their son deserved a little time to get healthy, so they welcomed him back home to heal. The parents searched the internet for tips about having a depressed son, they attended a support group, and had discussions about Michael coming home. They told each other things like: *People with mental illnesses aren't to blame. He is suffering and deserves support from his family, the same as folks with cancer and other serious diseases. We have to ensure that extended family and friends treat him with patience and respect during this difficult time. People with depression are sick and we cannot allow anyone to stigmatize our son by treating him any differently than a person with some other type of health crisis.* They tried to convince themselves this was all okay, normal for the circumstances.

In the psychiatric evaluation, Michael's mom was making eye contact, speaking directly to me, while sharing what her experience had been like a year before. She made a sideways glance at her son and paused. She took in a big breath and continued, "Honestly, Doctor, when we brought Michael back home, I want to say we were full of optimism and clarity about it, but I think we both had a nagging little voice in the back of our minds: *What if it's not so simple? What if he doesn't get better? What if time away from school doesn't help him get healthy?* My sister's daughter, our niece, she got depressed and moved back home a few years ago, and it turned into a disaster for her and for the whole family." She started to cry. "We were trying not to say it, but I think we were both thinking: *What if he checks out and never checks back in, like Ashley? What if instead of improving, he just sits at home making no progress?*"

She told me that she and her husband had been intimately involved, supporting their niece through the whole crisis, not at first, but as they perceived that Ashley's parents had become overwhelmed and were out of answers. As aunt and uncle, they tried to act as mentors. They tried to support her sister and brother-in-law. They moved Ashley into their guest room for several months.

Michael's mother related Ashley's story to me. Ashley had started off just like Michael. She moved back home from college, depressed, and everyone in the family was prepared to do whatever it took to help. She moved home, but it did not really help her get better. She stayed depressed and then she was caught drinking underage. It wasn't just one incident; she fell into drinking all the time, self-destructing right in front of her parents' eyes. She hardly ever got out of bed except to sneak out to the liquor store or a bar. Her parents had to drag her to see her counselor. Ashley's mother would call Michael's mother crying almost every day. They spent hours on the phone talking about what a nightmare it was having her daughter back at home. And of course, Ashley's mother was angry. She was watching her kid destroy herself and she just wanted to shake her and tell her to snap out of it, to get herself together.

Ashley couldn't do anything productive. None of the treatments they tried for the depression seemed to help her at all, even if they could get her to cooperate. She just sat there getting worse, and her mother was completely helpless. They spent three years in hell dealing with her. It was mystery to the entire family why Ashley became utterly incapable of getting back to normal for so long after she left school.

The two young people's lives seemed to run parallel, Michael's mom pointed out. They had each taken a medical leave of absence from college to deal with a mental health crisis. Each had failed to progress while living back at home. The start of Ashley's story paralleled Michael's perfectly. But the longer she stayed at home, the worse things got. She deteriorated to the point of drinking and lying in bed all the time. When she did leave the house, it was during the middle of the night, to sneak out to a bar. And while Michael wasn't doing anything like that as far as they knew, his parents were afraid that if he didn't get on the road to real recovery, that kind of deterioration would follow. How long could he sit steeping in depression, failure to function, and loneliness before things worsened?

"My sister would jolt awake during the night to the phone ringing and only then realize Ash had been gone from the house for hours, out drinking someplace. Drunken bad judgment led her into some dangerous situations: alone with a stranger in a dark parking lot, too drunk to get herself home and scared he was going to assault her, she ended up calling her parents to crawl out of bed and come find her before something happened. Middle of the night crisis situations became weekly rituals. Her parents finally said, *No More!* and refused to continue to allow her to deteriorate right under their noses.

"It took so much courage! I don't even understand how they did it. They ultimately made a list of their expectations, and held Ashley to them, but only after a long struggle to support her through the depression and addiction had failed. She finally got herself back together, but only after three years of decline and all those sleepless nights for her parents. It was their tough-love approach that made it happen, Dr. Deuter, and you were the one that told them it was what they had to do," Michael's mother concluded.

She had just confirmed what I suspected already: Michael's cousin Ashley was my former patient. I had had a meeting just like this one, a few years prior, and heard these stories then.

"We are relying on you to be able to tell us whatever you said to them," she added.

I remembered Ashley, but I wasn't sure what it took to get her parents to understand that providing her a place to live rent-free was part of the reason she continued to flounder and place herself in dangerous situations. She had plenty of money, a nice middle class lifestyle with free food and a comfortable air-conditioned bedroom, and only had worries in theory. Nothing especially bad had ever happened to her, just a lot of risk taking, and her parents believed that she needed to change before her luck ran out. Young people don't estimate risk like experienced older adults. And her parents were the ones shouldering the responsibility for cleaning up her messes, not Ashley.

Now here was Michael, not drinking or going out and placing himself in dangerous situations (at least not yet), but living out a strikingly similar lack-of-progress scenario. He came home to get well, and he wasn't making any progress toward improvement. His parents were beginning to think that giving him time was the wrong way to help him, that doing so could lead down a destructive path. His medical leave of absence might be useless, or even perhaps harmful. He hadn't appeared to improve after an entire year of rest and intensive treatment. On the contrary, it sounded like he had given up on going back to school.

I was lost in thought, trying to remember what I had said to Ashley's parents and trying not to react to the discomfort of the situation. They expected me to recall what profound advice I had offered to their family member, and I wasn't sure. To add to the discomfort, I couldn't really talk about what I knew of Ashley's case because I was bound to protect her privacy. I couldn't even confirm that I had been her psychiatrist.

Michael's dad brought me back into present awareness as I noticed he was nodding his head in agreement with what his wife was just saying a moment before. He kept the conversation going by adding, "I've had my suspicious that sick leave wasn't helping."

Michael spoke for the first time since they had arrived. "Dad, I just don't feel ready! Why is that so hard for you to see?"

Reacting in frustration, Michael's dad said to him, "Oh, I can see it alright. That's why we are here, son. That's the point. You don't seem to want to do anything. You never get out of bed, and we are at our wits' end."

In response, Michael mumbled, "You obviously just don't understand," and stopped talking.

His dad looked at me and said, "I can't say anything to him. I'm always wrong. He is upstairs in bed, barely even out of the room. Twelve months! And I'm not allowed to say, 'Hey, this isn't working.' If I breathe a word about it, he acts like I'm asking him to solve all the problems of the world. I just want him to get up out of bed and try something, just for a few hours a day. Now look how sullen he gets. He acts like I'm the bad guy for worrying. I think my response, *our* response, is pretty natural. We raised this kid. We paid for college, which he hasn't even finished. Now we provide him with everything he needs, and all we want is to see that we are doing something in his best interest. We just want to see some progress, so we know we're doing the right thing here."

He stared at Michael, who looked at the floor, defeated. He made no attempt to respond.

I thanked the parents and asked if they could wait in the waiting room.

I spent an hour with Michael after his parents had had their say. He perked up within a few minutes of their leaving the room, and seemed pleased to have an opportunity to speak for himself. Michael explained what he believed they couldn't understand: that everything felt daunting. He thought college was supposed to be one of the happiest times in a person's life, but he hadn't enjoyed it much. There was a lot of drinking and talking about inflated, self-important futures. Everyone was going to be a self-made millionaire before the age of thirty. He found his peers arrogant and maybe naïve. He doubted they would all achieve their dreams.

Michael didn't drink like his friends, and he didn't know what to expect in his own future, in contrast to their grandiose plans. He couldn't even hang with the conversations of his peers as they chugged beer and laid out their fantastic dreams. He had gotten to college and found that he didn't fit it. He didn't like his major, either. He had chosen pre-med, thinking high achievers like himself were cut out for medicine, but he didn't know if he was heading in the right direction. He didn't know if he had the confidence he saw in the doctors he worked with at his job. He had started to feel like he was in the wrong place, but couldn't think of any better ideas for a college major or a future career. That was when the depression hit – when he realized he might be in the wrong career with no other options. He had never battled depression before, so he thought the feelings might pass. Instead, things steadily continued to decline into deep depression, and he believed he had probably waited too long before asking for help.

He sought support at the student clinic on campus, and they placed him with a counselor. The staff told him adjustment to college was sometimes tough, and they assured him the counseling center helped kids like him all the time. He just needed to meet with a therapist every week, and soon he would figure everything out. Seeking treatment was the key step. The rest would fall into place. They seemed quite certain everything was going to turn out fine.

So Michael met with a young woman, barely out of college herself, he suspected. They sat in an awkward little room with their knees almost touching and she nodded along while he tried to tell her his woes, as he best understood them. One hour every week he talked and she acknowledged, but this didn't provide any answers. During his final session, Michael concluded he was wasting his time. That was when he decided to move home, imagining the answers would come to him with rest and time. Maybe he just needed to get out of the academic rat race and clear his head. Lower his stress. Although he had already begun to question the value of counseling, he followed the recommendation of the student health team and started with the new counselor when he returned home, and he liked her. She really listened and she gave advice sometimes. Advice was nice, and yet somehow not a solution. There were no concrete answers to his problems, he discovered. He started taking medication and he stopped crying. The worry lifted a bit. But why would he want to go back to college, even if he could go to class without wanting to cry? He was two and a half years into a major he doubted was right for him. Why take more classes in the wrong degree plan?

He said he had spent hours in bed since returning home, thinking, trying to decide what to do next, and he just didn't ever know for sure. So he didn't do anything. Nothing. He was waiting for inspired certainty before he made another move. He couldn't risk being wrong a second time.

"So, you went off to school, and you didn't feel like you fit in. It was stressful feeling that you were in the wrong place. For a while you were down and sad, crying and worrying, but now you're just not sure what to do next?" I asked. "Did the medication help you, then?"

"I guess so." He said. "Like I told you, I don't cry anymore. It hasn't been like that, with the crying, for a while. Maybe six months."

While he talked, I observed that Michael's mood appeared to be within the normal, healthy range, and had been this way for six months. *Why was he unable to function?*

Michael told me he thought he just needed more time, and that he would do more when he felt able. He said his parents needed to stop pressuring him, or else he would get depressed again. *Pressure? A year of rest didn't sound like "pressure" to me.* He was adamant that his motivation would return when he had rested sufficiently. However, I didn't think it was going to work that way. I had seen this problem with young adults too many times. They step into the sick role, and step out of the developmental stage of emerging adulthood. They stop growing, stop learning, and stop developing skills for independence. Once out of these roles, they don't go easily back in. Going back becomes too overwhelming.

Young adults like Michael and Ashley haven't had a sufficient number of experiences to build up their stamina for adulthood yet. It's like they started training for a marathon, and after just a few training sessions, had a serious injury. Now they are expected to get back out there and run, to keep up with the group that began preparing for the marathon with them, but they feel insecure, behind the race, and that they cannot compete. All the while, the clock is ticking and it feels like they will never be ready for the big race. They quickly refuse to risk failure, so they go back to bed for a year.

"What if it doesn't work that way? What if time off isn't the answer after all?" I asked. "You have taken an entire year to rest and feel better, but you're still not getting back to normal life."

"Are you siding with my parents?" he asked.

"Not at all." I reassured him. "But you had a plan to get better, and I'm asking if maybe that plan isn't working, and if you have considered going to Plan B. Is there a Plan B?

"I know I just need to wait, and I will feel better," he dug in. "I'm doing the best I can." He said his therapist understood he needed more time, and she had been encouraging him to avoid stressing himself out for fear he would relapse into depression.

A year was a long time to wait up in his room thinking and hoping for change. And here he was frozen in his "disability," but he didn't look like he was very sick with the depression anymore. The medication for depression had helped. He was just afraid to push himself forward for fear of relapse.

"What is it that your parents fail to understand?" I asked.

"That I need to be left alone. I will figure this out on my own," he said.

I didn't think he would. "I think you did a pretty good job of explaining it to me, don't you?" I asked. "Maybe I could meet with your parents and talk to them about what I understand, with your permission. Maybe I can help them see where you are coming from. Would that be okay?"

"Maybe," he said. "I know I can't talk to them. It just makes me feel worse. They are so worried and I don't know what to say to make them feel better, so I just don't want to talk about it. If you think you can help with my parents, I guess that's okay."

We scheduled an appointment for Michael's parents to come back in and talk to me without him. He said he didn't want to hear them talk about him, so we could meet separately. It made him feel guilty and defensive to hear what they thought about his problems. We would meet one time, before I knew Michael too well, and talk about what they could do to help him.

We needed to talk about how placing an adult child in the sick role could mean inadvertently sending that young adult upstairs to his childhood bedroom to stay. Unfortunately, I was seeing this problem more and more, as good parents lovingly supported emerging adults through a variety of health problems. Invariably, it was the resourceful, helpful parents who risked getting stuck with a kid upstairs. I sat down and made a list of what we needed to discuss.

When parents like Michael's come in, what do they need to know in that moment of crisis?

- *This is common, and growing in frequency. But people aren't talking about it enough. So even when your friends are in the same situation, they may not tell you.*

- *Emerging adults are wedged in between child and adult roles. It can be confusing to know when to "parent" them, and when to expect them to act like adults, especially when they are sick.*

- *Sick people can behave like adults.*

- *It's the lack of experience being adults that makes people topple easily when they are young.*

- *The culture around the way we "parent" young adults and the way we think about psychiatric sickness are both contributors to why young adults are now susceptible to this type of problem.*

- *Your son can sit up in his room for an entire year without necessarily being very sick at all. It's not certain that he has a serious mental illness, and that's what got him off track. Even if he does have a mental health diagnosis, it may not be the best course of action for parents to allow him to stay in the sick role indefinitely.*

- *You don't have to walk around on eggshells. Your child being "stuck" doesn't mean you cannot hold him accountable for working actively toward his mental health recovery. Parents fear that "stuck" kids may be fragile, but often they are not.*

- *You don't have to help him, but it's okay to continue to help if you believe it's the right thing to do.*

- *It can be hard for parents to know when an adult child is doing all he can do, and when he is capable of more.*

- *Assessing what your young adult child is capable of, and whether he is progressing, is easier than it seems at first. Allowing your child to do the wrong thing won't feel good to you. If you are a parent helping your emerging adult child and you are feeling resentful, you are probably enabling your child to do wrong things rather than helping him heal. Being supportive, by contrast, usually feels pretty good.*

- *If you step back, think, and plan, you can create a structure to get control over your life. Your adult child has to get control over his life, too.*

- *Getting things under control means you'll have to create structure, and keep your adult child accountable for doing his or her best. This is not the same as "tough love." I don't like that term very much. It's love with accountability.*

- *You'll have to decide how your support can be used, and what conditions apply. You'll have to be very clear about what help you can and cannot provide.*

- *You can't control your kid's thinking or their choices, though. Ultimately, your adult child has free will and will make decisions on his own.*

- *When your adult child is stuck upstairs, your job is not to rescue him. Your job is to make the rules and create a structure for how your money, house, car, etc. can be used to support him.*

- *When young adults are stuck, parents have to emotionally let go.*

PART 1

CHAPTER 1

---

18 Isn't 18 Anymore

During the 1960s in flat, dry, remote Cisco, Texas, Glen and Nancy were students together under gold-and-black football banners at Cisco High School. Not the sort to participate in football or cheer, the two teens who would later become my parents hung out in band and trigonometry. They spent four memorable years in high school, building toward the day they would graduate and officially transform into adults, and go out into the world as a duo. They fell in love over discussions of sine and cosine, and planned their future together long before ever walking across the stage to receive their diplomas. Falling in love and planning a marriage was a perfectly normal activity in the hallways of their school in that era. The quarterback might be expected to court the homecoming queen, as teens went out on car dates, shopping for a lifelong mate. Many found someone by graduation. In those days, the high school graduation ceremony was a line clearly demarcating the break between childhood and adulthood. Of course they were ready.

They were eighteen. Grown. Adult.

At age eighteen, my father was fully a man. He was free to join the Army, start a family, or otherwise make his own way. He could choose to work on his father's 200-acre farm, battling drought and willing seedlings to sprout in the Texas heat. Or he might try his hand at another career of his choosing. Either way, one thing was clear: eighteen marked the time to assume his adult role, and he was not to remain a child any longer. He was expected to be an independent, contributing member of society. He had to support himself. And so that is what he did. By the end of his eighteenth year, my father lived out on his own, he had started a career at General Dynamics and married my mom, and then within their first year of marriage, they became expectant parents. He was a grown up. His time had come to take the helm. The assumption of adult roles was not just encouraged, it was expected. He followed a fairly standard timeline for the day.

Perhaps as a young woman, my mom would not have been pushed out the door at eighteen. Had she not found a suitable partner for marriage, she would have continued searching a while longer. In which case she would have been allowed to stay at home until she married, if necessary. But even in that case, she still would have been working outside the home or helping the family in a variety of ways. Being an adult required making a contribution. My mother chose to become a wife and mother straight out of high school. She, too, had become a full-fledged adult, free to make her own choices and live her life according to her values and wishes, all by eighteen. Having completed her high school education and come of age, she had reached a transition point, a thin but clear line signifying her departure from childhood and entrance into adulthood. Her eighteenth birthday, her high school graduation, those were the signs she was qualified to become a grown up. She married, gave birth to a child, and took responsibility for her livelihood, her future, and her new household. It was a monumental year. Taking on these roles at her age was seen as a positive thing, not a tragic mistake as it might be seen today.

In their day, this was a typical picture of the transition from childhood into adulthood: the teen years gave ample time to prepare, they turned eighteen, and off they went into adulthood. A fairly straightforward transaction in most cases: children grew into adults as they crossed through a predetermined checkpoint with two milestones that occurred typically within the span of a calendar year: high school completion and coming of age. For those who didn't graduate, the eighteenth birthday marked adulthood just the same.

Sure, some people headed off to college. In that case, some of the roles would be delayed until education was complete. My father's younger brother went off to college after high school, and so he waited a few years to marry and start a career. But the rest worked the same way. He went to school, he met a girl, and then they married at the end. The college students represented an exception to the usual eighteen rule. However, when their education was completed, the college-educated folks were back on the road to independence as quickly as they could get there. Unlike today, a twenty-two year old college grad would not have been encouraged (or perhaps even allowed) to move back home and live with his parents to "figure things out" in the 1960s. As a college-educated man, he would be expected to go out and find work. He might go home to help with the family business, but he would have been expected to earn his keep and make a valuable contribution. He would certainly not have been invited back into childhood; not at all.

Eighteen- to twenty-two-year-olds who weren't in school would generally not have been welcomed to crash at their parents' house in some kind of in-between stage of neither-childhood-nor-adulthood as they might nowadays. And certainly mid-twenties graduates were not invited to loiter around the family home for long – a far cry from the modern standard. Teens became adults, and although some paused for education, soon afterward, off on their own they went.

Today, young people are often encouraged to live in an in-between stage. Young adults are welcomed to stay with parents and discouraged from going out on their own, because they are seen as generally unready. After teen and before "adult," we have created another stage: emerging adulthood. Even if you don't use the term, you see this new stage all around you. Society lets young adults function as kids well into their twenties.

Emerging adulthood has been adopted by many cultures (especially "Westernized" ones) as additional time for growing up. The shift in culture is unmistakable. Things are different than they were a couple of generations ago. Eighteen year olds are not considered adults anymore; they are teenagers, edging into adulthood in baby steps. They are neither adult nor child. They take on a mix of roles and responsibilities of both, but which of the roles they take is often subject to interpretation by their families. Twenty-somethings may live away from their families, but still receive help paying their expenses, or they might live at home while navigating education or working in the early stages of their career. It seems we have taken the in-between once held for students like my uncle, and applied it to everyone between eighteen and their mid-twenties, or in some cases even longer.

Today's twenty-somethings have many of the rights of teenagers, and only a limited range of the responsibilities of adults. We deem them unqualified for independence, and see them as late-stage children. Older adults say twenty-somethings are immature, incapable, sheltered, and still need time to grow up. The generation gap is written about in business journals, as sixty-somethings try to learn how to work with twenty-somethings. So much has changed in such a short time.

But the change doesn't just suddenly occur at age eighteen; so much has changed about parenting and communities. Kids stopped playing outside alone a long time ago. Parents started overseeing the school day from afar and structuring play for kids during "free" time. Kids spend most of their time under the direct supervision of an adult. As a result, kids and parents are different than they used to be.

This morning, I put my fourteen-year-old son on a plane for a school trip. In days leading up to the departure, parents texted me, fretting about the choice to let their kids go spend six days exploring marine biology in the Florida Keys. Hurricanes, sharks, what if he gets lost, she's never flown without me, twenty-three fourteen-year-olds and one chaperone teacher... Inside the airport, parents hung around for a full hour to see them off. I doubt anyone was thinking, "Wow, these teens are practically ready for adulthood." Nobody was wondering if they would solidify plans for a career, or fall in love with a classmate on this trip and start the march toward building an adult life as a result.

In fact, his grandparents, the same ones who came of age at eighteen, still see their teen grandson as a kid. The school trip makes them a little nervous. *Are you sure you want to send him off like that? Is he ready to be so far from home without a parent? Can't you go along on the trip with him?* They wouldn't want to see my kids released into adulthood by the end of high school. After the trip, when my son inevitably proclaims that he wants to study marine biology, he won't be taken seriously. If he comes back in love with a classmate, his grandparents will probably laugh about it. It's just puppy love. Most of my parent peers aren't attempting to march their kids toward adulthood. They're just trying to get them into a good college.

College is now like a prolonged summer camp after high school, four plus years to ease into grown-up life slowly. We don't want our eighteen-year-olds thinking about marriage, family, or full-on adult independence. Nobody will want to encourage them to pursue the whims of teen romance, or the fanciful ideas they will hold about careers either. Our family and our culture won't assume that most of our kids are ready for the responsibilities of adult life until at least their mid-twenties. If any one of my three kids decided to move out and start adult life, complete with career and family, when they were just out of high school, they would surely be dissuaded by every one of their family elders on both sides.

The 1960s weren't so long ago, and yet everything is new. From grandparents to grandchildren, all the rules about how one becomes an adult have been turned upside down. Just over half a century is a relatively short time for such a dramatic cultural shift, and the newness of the "mid-twenties is adult" expectation may explain the problems we are seeing with it. The transition to adulthood looks to be full of turmoil, confusion, and fear of change, by young people and their parents alike. When we did away with the old definition of an adult, we didn't define a new rule distinctly. There is quite a lot of gray area in the new system.

Eighteen was a clean line. High school graduation coincides efficiently with that age. The break was tidy. Everything came together crisply to define that neat line. But where exactly is the "adult" line today? Is it college graduation at twenty-two? Some would like to think so, but for others that still seems a bit on the young side to take on all of the responsibilities of grown-up life. Do we want our twenty-two year olds to head to the chapel immediately, and then start having babies? And what about the kids who don't go to college, or those who start higher education and then drop out? Or the ones who go on the seven-year plan? Or go on to a master's degree or a doctorate (which are both increasingly popular)? What about military servicemen and women? Are they adults when they sign on the dotted line with the recruiter? After completing basic training? After their first deployment? Certainly our military personnel have taken on many, or even most of the roles we expect of an adult, but even then they may not feel ready for marriage, family, or some of the roles outside of work that constitute adulthood. Where is the universal adulthood line now? It's hard to say.

The truth is, we no longer have a clean, black-and-white line that defines adulthood. To understand why, it's important to acknowledge that the line we drew before was based on a hypothesis drawn from common sense, not science. Observed from the outside, human development looks to be complete by around eighteen in most cases. Eighteen made a lot of sense as the choice for most reasonable people. An eighteen-year-old has almost always reached their full physical size, completed sexual development during puberty, and has gained enough experience to function reliably in the world of work. At this age, human beings are strong physically, and worldly enough to make it on their own without the supervision and oversight of their parents. In the absence of a brain scan, eighteen looks pretty grown up. But is it really?

CHAPTER 2

Blurring the Lines.
When Is an Adult an Adult?

A sobbing mother collapses on the sofa in my clinic. She just found out this week that her twenty-year-old daughter Sophia is thirteen weeks pregnant. "Her life is over," she proclaims.

Sophia still lives in her parents' home. She has been taking classes part-time at the Alamo Community Colleges for three semesters and working at a local taco shop three to four days a week. Her boyfriend Josh goes to UTSA, a hometown four-year college, and also works part time. Like Sophia, Josh still lives at home with his family. They met as high school sweethearts, drawn together by conservative values and a shared faith. While they intended to wait until marriage to begin a physical relationship, it didn't turn out that way. Both strict Catholics, they didn't support birth control, and then three months ago the accidental conception took place. They could not abide babies born out of wedlock. With a firm push from their parents to raise their child together as a traditional family, they decided to marry.

The wedding will take place in three weeks. "She's just a child herself," wails her mother in a state of grief.

Sophia's mother recalls that she was only one year older than her daughter is now when she married and started a family, "We all got married by twenty or twenty-one in those days. It was normal then. We didn't want to be old maids. But it's different now. Kids, they just don't grow up as fast as we did. Sophia is not an adult at age twenty. She is not ready for any of this."

"Why do you say she's not an adult?" I ask her, curious about how she pushed for her daughter to marry while not believing her to be a ready adult.

"I don't know. Society has changed. Schools don't get kids ready for life anymore. And the parents don't let them learn on their own. I followed the culture and I never prepared her. I didn't even teach her how to cook a proper meal. I feel like I failed as her mother. I didn't let her learn, I protected her from anything too grown up. I kept her close to me all the time and made decisions for her. I think I just wanted her to have plenty of time to enjoy being young. Sophia was sheltered, and now she's just not ready to be a mother," she wept loudly, this time uncontrollably.

She wasn't just saying Sophia was immature. She was claiming twenty-year-olds used to be adults in previous generations but that it is no longer the norm. She blamed herself and the changes in our culture. I tended to agree with what she was saying about how things have changed, but I didn't agree that she had failed.

Why are twenty-year-olds these days somehow less adult than their parents were at the same age? Human development hasn't changed. There is no difference in the physical maturity of a twenty-year-old from back then compared with today. If something has changed, the change is cultural.

The word *adult* has more than one meaning. In some contexts we use it to refer to full physical development, and in other cases to readiness for mature, responsible roles. When non-human animals mature to full size and are capable of reproduction, we label them as "adult." But with humans, adulthood is often defined by a series of societal roles. If we used sexual maturity as the definitive mark, kids as young as twelve would be taking on independence. Clearly twelve is premature by all reasonable social standards. We don't allow emotionally immature young people to rush forward into adult roles because we want them to have more time to get ready. According to the societal definition, adults are emotionally and financially independent. They can marry, vote, serve in the military, purchase cigarettes and mature content, and make legal decisions for themselves.

Adolescence was first recognized as a stage of development in the early 1900s. Prior to that, physical maturity was the only recognized marker for the onset of adulthood. Teen boys went off to war. Girls were allowed to marry, often much older, well-established men. Until adolescence was recognized as a distinct and necessary stage of development, puberty and physical stature were the only measures used. Adolescence seems obvious today as the stage in between childhood and adulthood, a time for mastery and maturation. Although adolescents appear outwardly to have obtained many of the attributes of an adult, we now universally accept that teenagers are not adults. Teens are unready for full-on independence, and they require support and supervision from caring adults for several years before we deem them ready for independence.

Still, the exact onset of adulthood is an elusive concept in many cases. Teens don't adopt grown-up roles en masse, they pick them up one at a time along the way. Sixteen-year-olds in the U.S. can drive a car and hold a job. In many states, including my own, seventeen marks the age of consent for sexual activity. Eighteen affords legal rights, the ability to marry without parental consent, and most of the rights we associate with adulthood. But the legal drinking age is twenty-one. One must be twenty-five to earn the right to reserve a rental car, and thirty-five to run for president of the United States.

Research on brain development gives new clues to when scientists should draw a line and say, *Adulthood starts here*. Turns out, there *is* a time when the brain is finished. It occurs some time near the mid twenties, when the myelin sheath, the coating that surrounds dendrites (nerve cells) completes its development. Consequently, this is also the same age when impulsivity drops and decision-making improves, a fact long known to the actuarial scientists who track auto accident statistics. The case for the onset of adulthood in the human brain in the mid-twenties is in fact more supported by research in a variety of fields than puberty or eighteen or twenty-one, or any of the arbitrary numbers which had previously signified the onset of adulthood.

Automobile insurance companies don't read neuroscience research, but they have been ahead of us all for a very long time in identifying the shift from impulsive teen to responsible adult. How did they do this? They used actuarial tables: statistics showing the average rates of auto accidents and risky driving behaviors. And what did those statistics show? That around age twenty-five, it's safe to allow a young adult to rent a car and it's safe to lower her insurance rates without taking a bath on the cost of paying out claims. Judgment improves in the mid-twenties, on average, as most brains become fully adult.

However, twenty-five hasn't replaced eighteen as the magic number marking the onset of adulthood. We no longer have eighteen. There is no universally accepted line that marks adulthood today. Young people are a hodgepodge of teen and adult traits. While many high school grads go on to college and finish in their mid twenties, others go straight out into the adult world. Eighteen-year-olds, or even younger teens, make reliable workers and have already begun to transition in small steps toward adult roles. Because adults younger than twenty-five can take on many or most of the roles to count as fully grown, no one is advocating fully moving the age of accountability up to age twenty-five. While the process of becoming an adult is completed around twenty-five, the onset of adulthood is not simply a moment in time, as if a light switch has been flipped on when it had previously rested in the off position.

Societal adulthood involves obtaining most of the roles associated with maturity. Adulthood comes on gradually, more like a dimmer switch being incrementally pushed upward toward the top. Past some point, the lights are bright enough to see your way. At that point, it's good enough to count as adulthood. The gradual climb toward neurologic adulthood begins at puberty, as early as age ten or thirteen. By eighteen, most teens have achieved enough maturity to be entrusted with a wide range of adult roles. Many older teens can tackle full adulthood, just as they could in the 1960s. They can join the armed forces, marry, and start families. The real difference today is that the elders in their communities might be more apt to discourage them from doing so, not that they are any less capable.

For Sophia, a dramatic jump will occur over the next few months. She will marry and move out of her parents home, begin to run a household with her new husband, and soon after take on the responsibilities of parenting. By the end of a year, Sophia will most certainly have achieved sufficient responsibility to fit the role of an adult in society. This will be especially true if her mother upholds her commitment to let go and allow Sophia to handle her own responsibilities and be accountable for her own life. Given the obligations to take on, she will do what is required to take care of her baby and her household.

It would be easy, after talking with her mother and hearing how Sophia lacks confidence and experience, to assume that she will be incapable of taking on the responsibilities in front of her. But in fact, becoming a responsible adult requires opportunity and experience more than any outward signs of maturity. Sophia will take on the roles in front of her when circumstances require her to do so. She will learn what she needs to know, and handle for herself what her loved ones stop doing for her.

She will do this because adulthood is a series of roles, and she is poised to step into them now. If she were not pregnant, not pushed toward marriage by her own beliefs and those of her family, and not taking on so many adult roles all at once, it is reasonable to imagine that Sophia might remain in an in-between state, more like a teenager than an adult, for the next five years. She would be likely to live at home and continue allowing her mother to solve her problems. She would be a student and a part-time worker, and likely continue asking her parents for regular advice to navigate the daily responsibilities of community college and food service work. On this alternative path, Sophia would get there eventually, but the circumstances of her life would not force her into mature roles as quickly. In the end, becoming an adult is all about what is being asked of her. And she will carry the load she is given, whether it is light or heavy. She will adapt.

CHAPTER 3

Your Neighbors' Best-Kept Secret

My practice is in San Antonio, Texas, the seventh largest city in the United States. And although the city approaches two million residents, it's amazingly like a small town in many ways. In certain circles, everyone seems to know everyone. I have to manage my schedule carefully so people won't run into their first cousin or their neighbor or co-worker when checking out after an appointment. This is especially true of Alamo Heights, a neighborhood/township where everyone knows everyone. In Alamo Heights, one of the more affluent areas of San Antonio, the parents of college kids all seem to harbor the same secret: their kids are struggling in one way or another. Alamo Heights is a relatively closed community. Many of the families who live there have been part of San Antonio's elite for generations. It's a small town within the heart of a city, and any problems that occur out in the open might be the subject of gossip or scandal. And so, minding one's privacy is encouraged, even expected.

Jacob's recent struggle was a typical example. He grew up a member of a well-connected Alamo Heights family. At twenty-two, he took a medical leave of absence from college in another state and he went into rehab for OxyContin and heroin addiction. People in the area know that there has been a growing epidemic of opiate related deaths, but users' names aren't revealed until a tragedy occurs. Jacob didn't tell anyone back home about his addiction except his mental health team, because he and his parents were certain everyone from the neighborhood would ostracize them. As one of his care providers, I was privy to the facts, but even the family's closest friends were kept in the dark. No one could possibly understand. Their friends and family members were all definitely thriving, they assured me. All the other peers went off to college and took on adult roles by storm. They were handsome, athletic, and intelligent beyond measure. They attended prestigious universities and earned excellent marks. None of his peers were having these embarrassing issues.

But I knew something I couldn't tell them, because I am bound by confidentiality. I knew some of Jacob's peers and their secrets. They weren't all taking the world by storm. One of his closest childhood friends kept dropping down to part-time student status without permission and lost his scholarship, but he kept that a secret. To friends in the neighborhood, he lived a glamorous life off at school. He may not have been a heroin addict, but he wasn't doing as well as Jacob believed. Another of his high school classmates faced legal charges for an alleged sexual assault. Nobody knew about that either.

Even the most stellar examples of successful students he referenced in comparison to his own failure were not what they seemed. In fact, he often spoke of his cousin Bella, holding her up as an example of how his peers all surpassed him. *Bella would never use drugs, and she is on path to graduate from an outstanding university, and then go on to a competitive graduate school program. She studied abroad and won all kinds of awards.*

Bella was the standard by which Jacob assessed his failures. But I had been seeing Bella's younger sister for six months prior to Jacob's visit, and I knew Jacob was wrong. Bella wasn't perfect, not by a long shot. What he saw on the outside, the perfect image of college success, didn't represent what was going on behind the scenes. Bella had been in trouble since she started college. While her grades were good, her behavior was out of control. She had repeatedly been caught spending thousands of dollars on her parents' credit cards without permission. When they took away one card, she would get hold of the new one and memorize the number. Sometimes she disappeared for days on end, and it was unclear to her nuclear family whether she was in danger when she went missing, or if she was just being spoiled and rebellious. The last time, she went off on a weekend trip to the islands and let Dad foot the bill.

Jacob's "evidence" to support his feeling that he was falling behind the group was skewed because everyone was hiding their problems. Even Jacob himself came up as some other young man's example, cited to demonstrate how the grass is greener for someone else.

Across the country, neighbors and friends similarly hide addiction and mental health problems. Stigma and shame fuel secrecy. Young adults leave the nest, and then what we hear of their successes or failures is often pre-screened for public consumption by them or their families. You may look around and believe that you see a large number of eighteen- to twenty-two-year-olds functioning impressively as full-on adults. They graduate from high school and go off to higher education at some illustrious place you never could have gotten into, or get astounding jobs. They move out and move up and move on. Right?

They may make it look easy, but using education as a means to launch into adulthood doesn't always work. It's not always so simple. After fighting for the best grades, spending dozens of hours on test prep, padding resumes with extracurricular activities, and then finally getting into the most impressive university on their respective wish lists, too many kids just don't make it all the way to graduation. The college dropout rate is absurdly high. Studies show that only two out of five students enrolled in four-year colleges will complete a degree within six years. While some students are on the seven-year plan, many won't complete their programs at all. Only about half of students have a degree at the six-year mark. That statistic alone is enough to call into question all the young people who believe they alone are floundering.

Recent statistics show that as many as 50% of eighteen- to twenty-four year olds live at home with their parents. Articles in various fields speculate as to the reasons for the rise in young adults living at home. Some say it's the economy – that young people cannot afford to rent an apartment or buy a house because the costs are too high or their pay is too low. Others call our current generation of young people lazy or entitled, or say they are overgrown children who are still too attached to Mommy and Daddy. Still others assume that young people have gotten wise, and decided they can stockpile a little cash by staying at their parents' houses a while longer, especially in this era of families communicating well and getting along joyfully. The nuclear family life is extended because people have become so mature and loving and pragmatic.

In a given case, any of these speculations may prove accurate. But in a clinical mental health office, where families come to deal with their secret problems, far more often it's those family secrets that drive kids to move home. The young adults here live at home for one very specific reason that no one likes to talk about: they couldn't make it out in the real world. They tried, and they failed. They started out on a path to leave the nest into adulthood, and they fell down in some dramatic way. Depression, anxiety disorders, and addictions top the list of reasons kids don't make it on their attempts to launch via college. Some kids just can't cope. Some develop somatic physical complaints from stress. Others don't manage to go to bed at a reasonable hour or get up every morning for class without the rhythms of a family household to create structure. When they stay at home and attend classes locally, it's common for kids to fail to get themselves to the campus on class days at all. I have even heard of students who would leave home in the morning as if following the schedule, only for their parents to discover later that it was all a ruse and that their child had stopped going to classes after the first week. They hide their failures from their parents and lie to avoid punishment like defiant teens.

Not all eighteen-year-olds go to college; some go to work. But even those routinely end up back home with parents. The young adults who start out in jobs and careers struggle to make enough money to support themselves, despite often being responsible and ambitious. Earning enough money is not sufficient to overcome a lack of life experience, and good earners may make spending mistakes. Hardworking young people, thriving at work, may still rack up crippling debt and move home. Others won't handle the pressures, or may fail to respect their supervisors and get fired or quit. Becoming an adult is not as easy as it sounds. Struggle is common.

For those who don't live in the fish bowl of a community like Alamo Heights, you need only look to social media to provide the same experience. Everything is presented in its best light. The people are all as beautiful as their vegan meals on Instagram. Nobody is telling the whole story, laying out details of how they slept half the day, missed work, and cheated on their diet by eating a half-gallon of their favorite vanilla ice cream. Everyone around you seems perfect and successful and flawless. But you know you are far from flawless.

When the neighbor's twenty-something moves back home to live, scholars may speculate that they just want to save money on rent, or that they are being a bit lazier than previous generations. But in my office, people are telling another story. And not all the young adults I hear about in mental health clinic are mental health patients. Many are the children or siblings or cousins or family friends of stable patients and they have no mental illness at all. Or, when young adults are seeking treatment for themselves, they may be struggling with adjustment, or minor symptoms of depression and anxiety. Others are coming for an emotional crisis, stage-of-life problems, or are dragged by parents because they watch Netflix and play video games all day instead of looking for work. But across the board, the stories I hear share one thing in common: kids move home because their plans didn't work out. They move home to figure things out and regroup. They move home for financial and emotional support, while they try to comprehend what went wrong.

The plans don't work out around 60% of the time, if you follow statistics. But when you or your young adult loved one stumbles, the messages around you tell you that you are the lone failure in the group. Everyone else is either tearing it up, or moved home to save a little cash before taking on their next gig as master of all things.

If our culture is to find solutions for the blips in the transition to adulthood, it will be of the utmost importance to begin a more honest dialogue about what so commonly goes wrong. Opening up discussions about mental health problems and addiction is one part, but we also need to welcome general discussions of vulnerability and personal imperfections among people of all stages, including young adults. Their futures may look bright, but things can still sometimes be hard. It's time to stop pretending and get real so we can see the problems and solve them.

CHAPTER 4

What Is "Stuck"?

Like a growing number of young people, Danielle found herself unready to be an adult at the age of eighteen. Off to college, overwhelmed, and back home to stay in a flurry of six months, her head was left spinning by the whole series of events. She had never imagined she was destined to end up in her old bedroom, Spurs dance team posters still on the wall from her high school days. It was supposed to be college and fun, then an impressive business career in the big city. That was how it was done, she had always told herself.

She started having trouble as soon as classes began her first semester. Professors were boring and disorganized, and they were terrible teachers. In every course, some old guy in a bow tie or young woman with a shaky voice just stood at the front of a giant lecture hall droning on. Classmates sat in a sea of strange faces, never making eye contact, looking as though they all wanted to crawl back in bed. Danielle slept through a few classes, and then she stopped getting up and going at all. She couldn't bear the discomfort. It was awful. Her roommate disappeared to a boyfriend's apartment. Then Dani went to bed and stopped getting out of the room much at all. She stared mindlessly at re-runs of Adult Swim cartoons. She played the Sims on her laptop. Text messages from parents went ignored. No one knew she had stopped attending classes. Before she knew it, she had missed most of the semester's seminars, and then missed exams, too. She was under water and had no solutions. By the time she moved home, Dani and her parents were calling her failure to function "the anxiety disorder."

Dani saw a counselor as well as her long-time family doctor for a prescription SSRI (selective serotonin reuptake inhibitor), which treats anxiety and depression. She met with the counselor one hour each week, she took two pills every day, and she waited to feel better. Six months passed. She decided to let the counseling appointments trail off, because nothing was getting accomplished by repeating her story of college failure, and there was no point at all to digging into her generally stable childhood upbringing. She didn't have anybody to blame, so she blamed "the anxiety disorder." Whether the medication helped was uncertain. Little adjustments and big changes in the medication failed to produce dramatic improvements. She tried several different meds, but none of them changed things. If any of those meds did help at all, the effects were subtle. But since she could only blame anxiety for her failure, she thought she would keep taking the pills every day to see if she found the confidence and the drive to try again. What else could she do?

Without the weekly therapy appointments, she didn't go many places. Prescription meds were handled in fifteen-minute check-ins that first came once a month, and then slowed to once every three months, and those felt like a waste of time. *Try another pill. It probably won't work either.*

She didn't know what to do with herself anymore. When she lived at home before starting college, she had been a full-time high school student. Her life ran on the school schedule—a regular bedtime and up at six a.m. every weekday, and then up late and sleeping in on weekends. The external structure of school had created a natural order for her life. No more school meant no more order. Minutes, hours, and days bled together. Without any place to be, her days and nights had become a blur of sleep for an hour or two or three, intermingled with distracting TV and internet. And in that state of lost, frustrated inactivity, she sat, restless but unmoving. No motivation came. No drive. Dani was stuck up in her room wasting time, still waiting to feel better. Her life was reduced to the bedroom and the dinner table, with only an occasional outing to pick up something for her parents. She took up cigarette smoking, just to have something to do. At least she had a reason to get out when she went to buy a pack of cigarettes at the corner store.

Month after month passed, and her mom grew worried. She took Dani to a new counselor to try again. Three months later she quit that one, then nothing much changed for two more years. Still she sat. Stuck. Talk of returning to college stopped. No one spoke of career. Dani and her parents just assumed she suffered with disabling anxiety. Why else would she be like this? No life, no aspirations, nothing. Just the rotting shell of a young woman who had once been full of hopes and dreams for the future.

Dani was stuck in the sick role, but stepping away from her adult responsibilities didn't seem to be helping her get better. In fact, she seemed to slip deeper and deeper the longer she stayed there. There was no place to get a foothold to help her climb out of despair. When friends or family asked what Dani was up to, or how she was faring, her parents would make jokes about young people these days, or change the subject. They had no idea how to comprehend, let alone explain what had gone wrong. They were scared and confused about Dani.

How on earth could this happen? Dani had never had any problems growing up. Why was her entire life on hold and failing to progress? Anxiety seemed to have claimed her and taken away everything.

Dani is not the only one stuck at home, receiving treatments that don't help. Moving home seems a natural step for a struggling student. Taking medication seems reasonable for a person suffering with anxiety. But *home* and *meds* don't help everyone. Some young adults like Dani, instead of formulating a new plan to take on adulthood bit by bit, opt to return to childhood roles and behaviors. They return to their childhood bedrooms complete with their childlike decor on the walls. They fire up the old Xbox and laptop and they park their butts on their Barbie beds, and there they may sit indefinitely.

Whatever the initial path out, and whatever the path back, for most of the young people affected, getting stuck at home starts off as an attempt to double back and start over. They start off, they fall off, and then they try to start over. Some of the young adults who end up stuck in an un-adult role moved back home in a crisis. Depression and anxiety are commonly blamed as primary causes. Some of those who are stuck were caught up with drugs or alcohol abuse. Still others came home for an unnamed problem, an invisible barrier between them and life success: they got placed on academic probation at college for failing grades, or they washed out of basic training, or got fired from a first job. Some racked up too much debt and couldn't stay afloat. At least a crisis offers a comprehensible reason why a person gets stuck back at home. But a crisis is not a prerequisite. Some stuck young adults came home because the rent was too steep, or simply because they completed some kind of training, even graduated from college, and then they came home to decide what was next, stagnated, stopped growing without understanding why, and never found a way out.

There can be countless reasons for going back, but no matter the reason, coming home creates a whole host of potential problems. Returning home can lead to going backward on the road to growing up. Lack of structure, comfortable parental support or conversely, parental resentments, can all contribute to getting trapped back at home.

In high school, most teens were marching toward a goal of adulthood. They were focused on graduating, or applying to college. These goals were externally defined, and as kids, they were constantly reminded to move toward them. And they wanted to graduate. They wanted to go on to college. Time was moving through a series of stages, marked by semesters and academic years and diplomas and graduation ceremonies. Now back at home, especially for those out of school, there are no semesters, no goals, no external pushes to get applications in by deadlines. There is simply a partially formed young adult, lacking in plan, structure, or skill, trying to sort out what she should do next, and often not progressing very successfully.

The act of moving home, apart from any diagnosable mental problem, creates conditions that lead to inertia; but moving home because you're sick with depression or anxiety or bipolar disorder or alcoholism compounds things further. Sicknesses require treatments and then time and healing. When a young adult suffers from a hidden illness like a mental disorder, how will she or her parents mark her improvements and readiness to return to functional roles? And how will they tease out the difference between being too sick to start over, and simply being scared of change, especially when she has yet to succeed in those adult roles? It can be hard to measure progress for a young adult like this. When is she healthy enough to return to a normal life? Wouldn't a young woman like Dani be afraid of failure after her first big plans for an independent adult life fell apart? How good would she have to feel to step out again, and how likely is she to get there just by feeling better in the safety of her parents' home?

Perhaps she thought that the family home was the best possible place she could go to get better. Mom's cooking and the familiarity of the family would provide her with the clarity she needed to heal and decide what would come next. She assumed her parents would provide nurturing and comfort, and that comfort would be a source of healing. Then Dani came home and her parents tried to support her like a sick person and saw that their love didn't heal her. She didn't get better. Love and nurturing was nice, but didn't solve the issues at hand.

Maybe nurturing her served as some sort of enabling. Parents might take the opposite stance and start with a hands-off approach. They would welcome her home expecting to find an independent adult woman, capable of clearing her own dishes and applying for jobs and figuring it out on her own. They would imagine she would be motivated to move forward. Then she doesn't function like an adult, because she doesn't know how, especially if she is eighteen or nineteen and never experienced adulthood in a successful way. And in that case, parents are quickly disappointed, compounding the feelings of being lost and sad. Either way, going home can have negative consequences. Disappointed parents aren't springboarding kids into success.

And then there are the problems outside the household that affect a young adult like Dani, such as problems in the way we diagnose and treat mental disorders. We are experiencing the height of diagnostic inflation in psychiatry. Labels like depression were once reserved for the most severe cases of sadness, low energy, and despair, in people who needed to be treated for months in hospital facilities. Anxiety disorders were crippling and people suffering with them could not live normal lives. Today those labels get applied more loosely, so much so that even the experts and leaders in psychiatry are often appalled. Anxiety and depression (the symptoms) are part of the universal human experience. Now these diseases can be diagnosed in almost anyone experiencing stress.

Dr. Allen Frances oversaw the writing of the *DSM IV*, which outlined the criteria used to diagnose all accepted mental disorders, and he has now written a book, *Saving Normal*, in which he argues that the diagnostic criteria he helped to create have evolved to become so vague that all of us could be diagnosed with something, from ADHD to bipolar disorder. I tend to agree. Dr. Frances points to how we have medicalized normal human experiences and now, with the help of our physicians to label us with diseases, too many of us seek to take pills to rid ourselves of all emotion that is unpleasant.

Our young people are most affected by these larger societal trends. They check the boxes of an internet test and self-diagnose some serious disorder. The "diagnosis" then becomes an explanation for why they can't overcome life's obstacles.

Clinical psychiatry is full of normal people seeking diagnoses to explain why life is so hard. Patients want medication to lessen the struggle, and the search for a pill to make us feel better is a culturally sanctioned action. You are told you can diagnose yourself from WebMD, and then "ask your doctor" for the prescription you saw on a TV commercial. You invest your time and money and you risk negative side effects of medications, but are never told that the treatments work best for the worst cases. Normal people aren't helped much with their painful emotional experiences by taking psychiatric medications. Contrary to lay people's perceptions, antidepressants aren't happy pills. Medications like Prozac don't make people happy. Medications only treat serious diseases. If you're neurobiologically healthy, medication of the type that we prescribe for depression or anxiety isn't going to do you much good. The loose diagnostic criteria for mental disorders allow us to diagnose anyone who is going through a rough time, but for the ones who aren't seriously sick, treatments don't work very well, if at all.

Young adults who get stuck at home, even the ones who are not waiting on a psychiatric treatment to make things better, rarely function well. A childhood family home is a place to relax and let someone else take care of you. Whether they possess a college degree or job experience, going back into their parents' home leads many young adults to regress, acting younger, less mature, and less responsible. Returning to their parents' home can lead to lounging around with their feet on the coffee table, leaving laundry for mom, and disregarding curfew. Impatient parents begin to pressure them to act like adults. And then being at home is not warm or supportive anymore. This dynamic can leave young adults overwhelmingly anxious and frozen in their tracks. They look to Mom and Dad to provide. They appear to work surprisingly hard at avoiding responsibility, and they appear unwilling to work at "adulting." They may act like defiant teenagers, refusing to participate in responsible adulthood. Stuck young adults can do their most efficient work at avoiding, manipulating, and skirting growth.

When a soft call of a diagnosis meets a failure to launch situation where a young adult starts bucking parental authority or deferring every tough decision to parents, medications don't do anything to help, and permission to be in an non-restorative sick role leaves them without much hope for recovery. What's the endpoint from there? Believing she is sick and will get better with medical treatments, a young adult like Dani moves home, wanting to get better. She follows all the instructions she is given: she sees the counselor and she takes the meds. Maybe she even changes her diet and starts an exercise routine. But she doesn't feel any better. And the situation becomes discouraging after a while.

From their young adult perspective, they feel overwhelmed and confused. Perhaps even ashamed. The plans meant to lead them into adult life have failed, and now they are trapped at home, terrified and embarrassed at the possibility that a high school classmate or family friend will approach them in the grocery store and ask, "What are you doing these days?" Stuck young adults don't know where to begin. Their parents are disappointed in them, and they are disappointed in themselves. Everything seems impossible. They wonder what is wrong, and they wonder how to fix their broken lives. They wonder why their parents lack compassion and why society has such unreasonable expectations. They want to hide underneath the covers and cry. If a mental disorder wasn't the cause in the beginning, one can certainly arise out of being stuck at home. Becoming depressed through inertia can add intolerable weight to the failures and confusion of young adulthood.

CHAPTER 5

Is It Mental Illness, or Is It Not?

Whether it's depression like Michael's or anxiety like Dani's or any of a whole host of other mental and behavioral problems, how on earth is a non-expert to know if an emotional problem rises to the level of a clinical mental disorder, requiring and responding to intensive psychiatric treatment, or if it's something else that doesn't require or won't respond to medication? People like Michael or Dani and their families just know that something is wrong. He isn't functioning. She cannot overcome. How do people outside the mental health treatment world tell the difference between a medication responsive condition and something else?

Depression can be a short-term symptom – in fact it often is. Most of us get a little depressed when we are overstressed, not sleeping enough, or experiencing grief and loss. We get anxious too. It happens almost every day, at least a little. In traffic, or when our teen is a few minutes late coming home from a party, we have a twinge of anxiety. Those sensations can be intense and unpleasant. Michael knew he felt down, and he found himself unable to keep up with his responsibilities. Dani's discomfort with college classes was so great that she couldn't manage to do what she needed to do. If they read through the diagnostic criteria on the internet, they would have seen things like "decreased concentration" and "poor appetite" – but *how* decreased is enough to make a diagnosis? How poor? How would they know whether their problems required treatment?

Lay people rely on specialists in the medical and psychological fields to tell them whether their problems rise to the level of a disorder, disease, or illness. Yet the experts rely on antiquated methods for making diagnoses. Mental disorders still use old-fashioned checklists full of unquantified, highly subjective phrases such as "change in energy," "decreased pleasure in activities," and "withdrawn". It's hard to know if you meet the definition by reading them. People with Generalized Anxiety Disorder may have "more fatigue than usual, irritability, worry, or problems with relationships." The problem with these criteria is that we all experience them from time to time. If you are excessively stressed from working long hours on a huge project for three weeks in a row, you might expect to be irritable, worried about completing the project, fatigued, and prone to relationship conflicts as a result. These criteria were written with the explicit caveat that only clinicians who understood the nuanced difference between normal and abnormal would use them.

However, medical culture around treating mental disorders has changed. If you go to a physician and report depression, most of the time you'll walk away with a prescription for an antidepressant. Rarely will you be offered reassurance instead. If you say you're suffering from anxiety, it will likewise be a prescription. Offering medication as the primary cure for unpleasant emotional experience has become the standard. Few depressed or anxious people would expect a referral for counseling or increased physical exercise from a primary care doctor or a psychiatrist, even though these non-medication treatments can be more effective than pills. Being told that your problem is subclinical and will clear up without medical treatment is rare, even when it would be an appropriate approach to treatment. And patients don't seem to want reassurance. Patients want antidepressants (and antibiotics).

Doctors pull out prescription pads like carpenters draw their hammers. We use the tools we have at our disposal. In fact, we often prescribe when we don't deem it necessary, simply because we believe that's what patients and their families seem to want and expect. This parallels the way physicians excessively prescribe antibiotics even when they suspect a viral illness, which antibiotics don't relieve. Doctors are caught between the medical knowledge and guidelines, and the desire to ensure that the patient feels adequately helped during the clinic appointment.

Often patients like Michael and Dani participate in excessive use of medication without realizing their role. They start out hoping that there will be a simple answer to the problems they are experiencing. If a prescription pill can fix it, that sounds simple and clear. Who wouldn't want to believe it could be so straightforward? Patients and doctors collude to take the easy way out. And it's not just a young adult patient who wants to believe a psychiatric diagnosis is the answer and medications will offer a cure. Their parents want easy answers. They want a problem that can be quantified and fixed up neatly. They hope the solution to the problem is as straightforward as checking off criteria from a list and running by the pharmacy on the way home.

In addition to the desire to have answers, parents are often trying to understand why their child underwent a dramatic change in mood or behavior. Mental disorders often onset in the teen or young adult years, at the same time that the brain is undergoing major changes that alter mood regulation and behavior. When their behavior is out of control or they cannot function in the basic roles they are expected to maintain, it's sensible for the parent of a young person to wonder if there's a problem requiring psychiatric help. Mental disorders claim too many of our youth. Suicide is a leading cause of death in teens and young adults. No wonder families and kids themselves participate in overdiagnosis and overtreatment. They're scared. The visit to a mental health clinic might be initiated by concerned parents, or by the young adults who are failing to thrive. The most common question: "Is this problem caused by a disorder we can treat?"

A young adult who only wants to hide under the covers certainly looks and feels depressed. She asks herself what happened to the hopes and dreams that motivated her to get through high school. Where is the zest for life, and where has her energy gone? Why doesn't she want to get out of bed? Why does she procrastinate searching for jobs? Why is she incapable of doing the things her peers make look easy? Can taking an antidepressant or talking to a mental health counselor get her life back on track?

The parent of a stuck young adult wonders the same. Why doesn't she want better for herself? Why does she lie in bed, avoid what needs to be done, and fail to move forward? They look at their child and recall simpler days, when he was a cooperative child following all the rules and expectations. It's hard to imagine that anything other than illness could explain such a dramatic shift in behavior. Can a mental health assessment tell us why? Can medication or counseling help her move forward?

What's the harm in getting a diagnosis and trying a treatment, anyway? It's worth a try to see if a medical care approach can change things. Maybe the antidepressant or the counseling will help. But what families and struggling young adults fail to weigh or fully understand is the risk involved. Of course they know that prescription antidepressants can have side effects, even serious ones, such as an increased risk of suicidal thoughts in people age twenty-four and under. So they'll ask about the side effects and look them up on the web, and they'll carefully monitor their children for signs of them. It often feels like a manageable risk. But what about the risks of hearing a medical professional tell you that you have a serious mental disorder? What are the risks of that? And what are the specific risks of hearing you have a mental disorder when you are young, lost, and overwhelmed, in the midst of forming an identity, and you're looking for answers to why you have failed at college or career? What consequences can the labels themselves have on the lives of impressionable yet overwhelmed fledgling adults?

Teens and young adults are seeking to form an identity. It's a large part of what they do. They break away from parents and they find out who they are, separate from the identity bestowed upon them by their parents. Sometimes they fall on their faces. On one hand, it's important to remember that mental health problems often onset in the late teen years or early twenties. Some of our struggling young people will be stricken with illnesses as they try to leave the family. But on the other hand, taking on adulthood is complicated in the best of circumstances. Moving out, taking on responsibility for a career, paying one's own bills for the first time, and solving one's own problems; becoming an adult involves a long list of important changes, each one with potential pitfalls. Newly minted adults have to learn to be the agents of responsibility and decision making in their own lives. They have to find answers for themselves, and do so with enough confidence to face the day.

Mental illness can affect mood, thought, or behavior, but doesn't necessarily cause disability. In fact, myriad adults with serious mental disorders such as major depression, bipolar disorder, and schizophrenia function in society, work full-time jobs, and support families. When a young adult like Dani starts to feel hopeless about having depression and believe she is unable to function, she sees herself as having a mental disability. She forms an identity around the illness and what she is unable to do. This makes her less *able* than she would otherwise be.

Illness identity can lead to far greater levels of disability for someone at the emerging adult stage. Consider, by contrast, Dani struggling as an adult at a different stage. For example, imagine her as a middle-aged professional mother of three who develops depression after twenty successful years in her career and as many years raising healthy, well-adjusted kids. She has ample experience to support an identity other than "depressed and disabled." And so, she is far less likely to give up on herself and go back to bed for good. She has responsibilities to meet, and she knows how to rise to the occasion. She has been doing it for years. She trusts herself to overcome and stay afloat. As an experienced adult, when depression comes on for middle-aged Dani, taking time in the sick role is productive. It helps her take care of herself. As quickly as she can, she gets back to work because she needs to pay the rent, and because she knows how to measure when she is feeling good enough to keep going.

But since the real Dani doesn't trust herself and hasn't identified as a capable adult, the issue of illness and identity is very muddled in her mind. She sees the lack of will as evidence that her abilities are limited. For her, youthful inexperience and lack of stamina represent depression just as strongly as a sad mood and low energy. She fails to realize that young adults screw up and stress out all the time, that some of what she is going through is simply normal when we are young. She's not the only one who avoids responsibilities when she feels overwhelmed. She's not the only one waiting for a "real" adult to show up and take responsibility for her out-of-control life.

Back in her childhood, Dani took comfort from following orders from parents and teachers. In adulthood, she looked up and found that there was no one giving orders anymore. She didn't really know how to be an adult and she gave up too easily. But the view of herself as a person with a mental disorder, fueled by her search for answers, changes how she interprets her response to stress. Instead of saying to herself, "Dani, don't be a slug. Get up and get going or you'll feel bad about yourself and Mom and Dad will pull you from school," she says, "I'm sick. I can't do the things other people can do, and I will never be able to."

With all of the forces at play, no wonder young adults who cannot function begin to look depressed. Becoming a grown-up is hard. But is Dani simply suffering from mental illness when she can't make adult life work, or is she perhaps also struggling to successfully navigate a natural stage of life? And more importantly, will mental health treatments help her figure her life out, or grind everything to a halt?

Even if Dani was not depressed to begin with, leave her stuck at home with her parents for long enough and she will be. Mental health diagnosis and treatment has the potential to make things worse instead of better, if it is not undertaken with great caution. Getting stuck and lost can make Dani depressed. Getting stuck can lead to a serious crisis of identity and functioning. Once depression becomes identity, there is little hope of breaking free of it long term.

It's a circular problem. Getting depressed causes young adults to get stuck, and getting stuck causes young adults to become depressed. However the problem starts, once on the merry-go-round of stuck and depressed (or anxious, or addicted, or acting out), it's hard to get off the ride.

CHAPTER 6

Trying Not to Push Them Over the Edge

J ustin got stuck at home. His decline started with partying and drugs. He went to community college with the mentality that it was thirteenth grade, just biding time to get through day by day. He was there to satisfy the expectations of others, trying to fulfill his parents' dream of affordable, practical education. So he entered the local program his high school guidance counselor recommended. Unfortunately, Justin took all his bad habits from high school with him to community college. There was no love of learning, no accountability, and no innate drive in him. He filled a slot and passed the time in class, and then he went out looking for fun. He hung out in bars or friends' apartments using whatever substances he could get. Anything would do, just to feel altered.

Responsibilities slipped by the wayside, replaced by elaborate lies concocting a school life. Parties and late nights replaced plans for the future. And then his house of cards fell. All that was left was a strung out kid and a lot of wasted time and money. His parents got involved when the problems became too obvious to ignore anymore.

After flunking out of his education and going into hiding at home for a while to dry out, Justin sought help. He got clean and sober with the help of an AA program and a sponsor. He attended daily meetings for a few months, and then dropped down to once or twice a week. He managed to stop the downward spiral of addiction by isolating himself from his party friends, leaning on the family to keep him away from the wrong folks, and seeking community with others in recovery. His recovery plan was solid and it worked.

When the whole school thing had unraveled, Justin could see that he needed more structure and accountability than was available at his college. It was the lack of these that helped him stagnate, and that had kept him there for too long. No one made sure he was doing the right things in college. There wasn't an adult in charge, holding him to his commitments. Justin was left on his own to perform and monitor himself, and he wasn't ready. Some teens develop an internal sense of motivation, an inner adult self that reminds them to do the right things. But Justin didn't have a grown-up anywhere inside, so he had needed something outside himself to keep him on track. Going to school relied too heavily on internal capabilities he didn't yet possess.

Despite his failure, Justin managed to forgive himself. He understood that he was an addict and that along with his impulsivity and tendency to seek thrills, he was not always responsible and mature compared with others his age. Accepting himself was easy. Explaining it to his parents? Not so easy.

Justin's parents had been terrified when the drug issues came to light. They had only realized something was amiss when they found him unresponsive on his bedroom floor and took him to the hospital. It was only after the emergency doctor suspected substance abuse that Justin's parents even considered the possibility of drugs. When he decided he needed help, they were grateful. They were panicked at the thought that addiction had so nearly taken their son, and vowed to do anything to help him stay clean. Doing anything included staying out of Justin's personal business, especially the details of his recovery plan and treatment. Doing anything meant not asking questions. Doing anything meant not pressuring him.

Justin worked his program, but that was all he did. Much like his time in school, he soon fell to the minimum standard and stayed there. He didn't work at a job learning skills or earning cash, he didn't help out around the house, and didn't return to education of any kind. The actual hours spent on recovery work dwindled over time to just three or four a week, but recovery was all he accomplished.

His AA sponsor Alan was a veteran in the addiction world, and he quickly recognized that Justin needed to do more than just get sober. Sobriety would be a platform to build upon, but it wasn't the whole program for a young man like Justin. Alan encouraged Justin to find a job or return to school, but Justin insisted he didn't have the bandwidth to do more than just stay sober. Even his sobriety could be tenuous, and so after a while, Alan recommended a mental health assessment. Maybe counseling or medication could enhance Justin's recovery.

Justin's mom came with him to the psychiatric evaluation because she had agreed to pay for it, and she still didn't trust her son to handle her credit card responsibly. Mom came into the assessment room when invited, saying she would be brief, and said her major concern was that her son seemed so fragile in his recovery. She said she could see that he was unable to do most normal things. Justin just couldn't tolerate responsibility. He would easily become moody and overwhelmed if pressured to do anything more than just stay sober.

She said she had learned not to ask anything of him. He seemed unable to cope with being pushed. She didn't want to push him over the edge.

When I asked if she meant that he would relapse into drug addiction if she pushed him too hard, Justin's mom said, "Oh, that or worse. I'm afraid I will find him hanging by a belt in his closet if I push him!"

The short interaction with Justin's mom left me confused. When I conducted the interview with him in private, he showed no signs of suicidal thinking. He had no past history of threats or acts of self-harm. He had never considered suicide and never hurt himself, even by accident, except for the drug abuse. Why on earth was she worried he was going to decide to kill himself now? I asked this question to Justin, and he rolled his eyes and said, "My mother can be a complete drama queen."

What seemed more concerning in my opinion than pushing him toward suicide was the fact that no one was pushing Justin at all. Justin wasn't growing. He was scraping the bottom, barely living a life. He appeared on track to live with his parents until he was at least forty, never working, having serious relationships, or changing in the least. Why would he?

Hoping to gain some traction, I referred Justin to counseling. In addition to his recovery plan, he would meet regularly with a therapist and talk about how his life was failing to progress. We set some goals for therapy- including trying to get him moving toward creating some kind of independent, grown-up life. Justin agreed that this was important.

But then after a few sessions, Justin's new therapist called to coordinate care. Instead of supporting a plan to push him forward, she too was worried about pushing him too hard. She thought that the few hours each week he was spending going to therapy and meetings was all he could manage, or else he would spin out into a crisis. What was it about Justin that evoked this reaction? I pressed her for evidence, and she said it was mostly her clinical intuition, a bad feeling, that made her worried. She didn't know exactly why.

I worried that Justin, like other young people forming an identity and standing still in the sick role, would gain nothing from waiting. In fact, precious time was being wasted. Every additional day that Justin passed in a state of "I can't" would solidify his identity as a fragile addict, prone to crack psychologically if pressed. What a dangerous message to send to a kid with no successes under his belt up to that point. No one thought he could grow. Why would he disagree?

His parents waited for their son to feel better, so he could get back out there and get his life on course. No one wanted to push him over the edge. No one wants to drive a depressed person deeper. No one wants to overwhelm a distressed young person further. Treatment professionals, therapists and doctors, might support this view. But seasoned addiction professionals like Alan are more likely to see how waiting shapes behavior and keeps people stuck. Being substance-free is a good start, but true recovery is more than that. Healthy people contribute.

Parents and providers decide that they need to give the treatments time to work. Whether it's medication, therapy, or a volunteer job, the consensus view is "go slow." We need to allow the medication to get into his system. We need to allow time for the therapy relationship to take root, trust to build, and growth to occur. Healing from a mental health crisis takes time, and young people need to be given time. This is in stark contrast to the tough love and accountability approach taken in the addiction world.

In a case like Justin's, the medical team, parents and professionals are likely to decide to just wait a while. A semester. Three months, six months, twelve months. They begin treatment and agree to a holding period. Following a medical model, everyone waits for signs of strength.

Missing from this approach is the strength training that might be prescribed after a medical health crisis. If Justin had gotten injured or required a surgery, instead of going to the hospital for a drug overdose, his recovery would involve a clearer plan for working out his muscles and getting him strong again. Rather than fearing what can go wrong if we push him, we should probably wonder how we can rehabilitate Justin and make him stronger. If he had hip surgery, he would be prescribed a course of physical therapy so he could use the affected muscles under the supervision of a specialist. Under such a program, he would get stronger. He would walk assisted, and then he would walk independently. Eventually he would be strong enough to run and jump again.

If the surgical recovery followed the philosophy of Justin's recovery from addiction, rather than doing PT and strength training, he would remain bed bound out of fear that he would injure himself trying to get up and walk. In the physical health arena, we have studies to show that staying in bed results in deconditioning, that refusing to use the muscles and tendons affected by surgery weakens the patient. When recovery from addiction or another mental health crisis keeps a patient confined to what is easy and doesn't push him too hard, likewise, he fails to get strong and he fails to achieve recovery. So why don't we routinely prescribe strength training for mental health recovery? Maybe we don't have enough research to prove that it works.

Mental health and addiction are relatively young sciences. The depth of research doesn't yet exist to answer many of our most important questions. What would a study show that compared, for example, people who work at a job during the first year after dropping out of college from drug addiction to people who go to meetings 3 to 4 hours a week, but achieve nothing else? Which group would fare better? The difficulty in studying such parameters is that behavior can be hard to mandate. Even studies of diet and exercise can prove tough because it's hard to get people to change behavior so groups can be accurately compared. As a result, we don't have proof to offer to families that Justin or someone like him would benefit from a firm push.

Justin's family and other families like them are only trying to protect their child. The trouble with mental health rehabilitation is that many family members and even treatment professionals don't know what is safe. When would sending Justin off to interact in the world be like a workout, and when would it be excessive or dangerous to his safety? What they fail to see is that Justin's recovery needs to include returning to the responsibilities of daily life. His habits and his self-image are being shaped while he recovers. This is how he gets stronger and rebuilds his life. Seasoned addiction sponsors like Alan know this, but don't have solid research data to prove it. Alan knows that Justin has to do some things that make him uncomfortable, and that he can do it safely. Behavioral health recovery doesn't just come on its own with time; the repair of a person's life involves stretching and growing stronger under the supervision of experienced folks who know the ropes. Justin needs to work, or attend school, to accomplish something every day, and begin to see himself as a functional member of society again. Sitting out reinforces the idea that he is unable to live a normal life. Rather than integrating functional roles into his recovery plan, he learns that recovery can be the only thing. He either lives his life, or he stays sober. Not both.

I think Alan and the addiction community are right. A young person like Justin needs the daily life functioning equivalent of physical therapy to help strengthen him after his crisis. In fact, I think this is true not only in addiction recovery, but in general mental health recovery as well. People have to get strong and get their lives back if they are going to have healthy outcomes.

CHAPTER 7

When It Comes to Mental Health, the Sick Role Is Overrated

J udith is a hard-working administrative professional. She prides herself in her dedication to keeping her office running smoothly day-to-day. She takes her role so seriously that she sometimes skips out on self-care and devotes her energies to the job, even when the best thing would be to take a day off. This week, Judith has a nasty sinus infection. It started with seasonal allergies, but has progressed to congestion that obstructs her breathing, and it feels like her head is in a vice day and night. She's taking medication, but the infection persists. Now for several consecutive days she has been unable to breathe when she lies down at night to go to sleep. She is up a dozen times a night to gasp for air and blow her nose. She has been coming to work fatigued, distracted, and lethargic as a result of insufficient sleep. Even though she is doing her best to keep up with the work, it becomes obvious pretty quickly that the entire office team would benefit, and that Judith would definitely benefit, if she took a day or two off to recover. By pushing herself to come to work eight hours a day instead of rest, Judith is draining her defenses. She is making it worse. Her daily work is not up to her usual standard, and her illness will likely last longer if she refuses to stop and rest to take care of herself.

Judith's boss and her co-workers can see the dark circles under her eyes and sense her frustration at having the symptoms continue too long. So they offer Judith some time in the sick role. They urge her to take the day off tomorrow to recover. It will obviously do her some good, and the office will run more smoothly when she returns. She is encouraged to step out of her responsibilities for a little while, acknowledge that she is under the weather, get the treatments and the self-care she requires, and come back stronger and better than before. Stepping out of her daily responsibilities will be good for Judith's broader health. Rest will hasten her recovery. It will aid in her regaining her usual state of physical wellness. Taking time away is going to be vital to the healing process.

This scenario isn't unusual. When a person is sick with a sinus infection, he or she is offered rest. Societies agree that when someone feels ill, it's often best to take respite and care for oneself. Pushing yourself when you have a crushing headache and sleep loss, or even fever and nausea from the flu, is likely to make things worse, prolonging the illness or making it more severe. We urge people to go home and go to bed. Take time and take care of yourself. Take a sick day. Don't worry about it. Feel better. It's obviously the right thing to do.

It's not just a standard to send folks home to rest for small illnesses. Long-lasting, serious diseases can respond to rest and time away from responsibilities. When people have major surgery or when they are diagnosed with cancer, we support longer periods of time away from responsibility. Large surgeries require rest and rehab for full recovery. Cancer treatments take a tremendous toll. Big medical maladies are deserving of a respite from responsibility. People having health crises deal with physical pain and anguish and cannot be expected to work long hours for days on end. They may need months of rest for a full recovery. Their families chip in and help them. Their workplace disability policies pay a percentage of normal salary. Systems are in place to assist people with time off. The sick role is a vital component of a functioning society. Sometimes people get sick, and when they do, they need space to get healthy again.

Likewise, when people get depressed or manic, develop panic attacks, or have a crisis from addiction and need time to heal, we encourage them to take time. That time may vary depending on the severity of the crisis. If an episode of major depression is causing sleep disruption, a week off work and a new medication prescription might aid in recovery. The sick role might allow time to clear out the offending problem, in this case sleep loss, in exactly the same way time off work allows Ms. Judith's sinus infection to clear. Or it might not. The course of depression can be similar to the recovery from an infectious illness, or it can be quite different. Unlike a sinus infection, depression doesn't always improve on a predictable time course. Depressions vary widely. Recoveries vary too.

Healing from a behavioral crisis follows a different course than the flu, and won't get better by taking a single sick day. But taking months to heal as is done for cancer may not help everyone who had depression. Mental health recovery may involve languishing for days and months without making any progress. The course to healing emotional illness is not equivalent to the wounds that scar over after surgery or the immune system that replenishes itself when the chemotherapy has finally ended. It can be hard to define the scope of rest that helps a person recover after a mental illness. Individual needs vary. Types of illness and personal needs fall on a wide spectrum.

Paradoxically, a mental or behavioral health crisis sometimes gets worse with rest. Exiting responsible roles may lead to isolation, marginalization, or shame. Depressed people can go off alone and wallow in their lonely sadness, not making meaningful strides toward recovery. Being alone may reinforce feelings of unlovability. Those with anxiety can strengthen their avoidance of whatever feels scary, and deepen their sense of fear. And others in recovery from addiction, people like Justin, can learn only to live without a substance, but not really learn how to live life as a whole, healthy person.

When Justin went home to take his time in the sick role and rest, he started to stagnate there. He became afraid to overdo it by continuing his regular daily activities, fearing his symptoms could return if he did. Since his parents couldn't measure his recovery by taking his temperature or having their physician order a CT scan, they too worried that he was too fragile to exit the sick role and go back to a normal life. Mental illness is a mysterious domain for a lot of people. Even loving family members don't know how the measure progress. That mysteriousness can imbue a psychiatric or behavioral disorder with a boogeyman-like quality, leaving sufferers and their families in fear that the disease is coming to get them if they're not careful.

Just yesterday I met with the parents of a college student on leave for depression. She went through a rough time and, in the midst of her struggle, she attempted to take her own life. That was many months ago. The elements that added up to her crisis and her hopeless attempt to end it all have come to light, and in my view they have been remedied. But the parents are having trouble taking my word for it. When their daughter was in serious peril the first time, they didn't know what signs to watch for. It happened right under their noses. Now, even though she is in the care of trusted professionals, for the parents depression still carries an enigmatic quality. They don't know how to monitor her progress; they never quite feel she is safe. As a result, they want her to stay in the sick role indefinitely.

The daughter, a young adult woman with a few years of experience on her own, feels ready to return to her life away from home and complete her degree program. She stayed with her parents as long as she could stand to feel like a child, and then she stayed a little longer just to help them feel comfortable. She can sense her isolation growing. She senses the urge to avoid getting back to normal life, and she doesn't want to give in to the impulse to hide in her childhood home. But the amount of time she's spent at home has not cleared away the monstrousness of mental illness for her parents. To them, it's coming for her at any time. They cannot shake the terror they feel, and sending her to live hours away from home seems dangerous.

Depressions can be much harder to wrap your mind around than the flu. One minute your loved one is laughing and smiling, then next minute she is contemplating suicide. So when a seriously depressed, suicidal person steps into the sick role, it's not uncommon for the patient and her loved ones to hope to see perfect happiness emerge before they feel safe sending her back out into the world. Good days and bad days won't cut it. Normal ups and downs take on a new meaning after the crisis. How can they feel safe facing a disease they don't understand? Where is the medical test that proves that the danger has passed? When is the disease in remission?

While people with depression certainly step into the sick role and back out again like those with other illnesses, mental illness makes the process complicated. At times, respite for those with depression is a welcome opportunity to facilitate recovery. However, rest and accepting the sick role are not universal salves for mental illness or addiction. The benefits of taking a sick day vary widely from person to person, episode to episode. Taking a day off may provide hope to one individual, but lead to feelings of loneliness, despair, or fear of relapse in another.

A mental health crisis has a long course, more like that of cancer recovery in most cases than like the flu. Going home from work or school and back to bed can lead to staying there for a very long time, perhaps months or even years, before it becomes clear whether resting is helping or hurting the course of recovery.

Permission to be in the sick role is thus trickier in mental health than in other areas of medicine. Sometimes people benefit from rest, but other times they benefit more from putting one foot in front of the other and continuing to live life day by day.

PART 2

CHAPTER 8

The Emerging Adult Stage

Oh my, how the world has changed since my parents met in high school during the 60s. Would these young people described in the previous chapters be in the situations they are in had they been born into a different era? It's worth revisiting here, in a bit more detail, how the stage of emerging adulthood came to be, how it works, and how it impacts the mental health of our twenty-somethings. As I said in Chapter 1, my kids are coming upon just about at the age my parents were when they met, and they appear to me to be at least a decade away from anything resembling adulthood. They are great kids, not spoiled entitled brats or anything like that. But they seem young. Sheltered. Inexperienced. Unready. They are doe-eyed innocents. For my part, I'm glad my high schooler will have more than the next few years to transform into a grownup. He needs that additional time. He's going to have a better adult life because he won't be rushing out the door to plan for a family and a career in a couple of years. He's naïve and idealistic still. He's got to get a little life experience under his belt before he takes on the world on his own. I'm glad the teen years have expanded into the twenties, to include the emerging adult years. By pointing out the mental health-related problems associated with the new extended adolescence, I don't want to mislead readers; I'm glad emerging adulthood has come along as a stage. It's good, when it works. We just have some kinks to work out, because it doesn't always work.

As an emerging adult, my boy will gain extra practice under supervision. He will have educators and parents and mentors to guide him while he apprentices as an adult for a few more years. More practice is a welcome shift. This way, he can gain some skill before being released to his own devices. Those years will leave him, will leave all of my kids and yours, better prepared. I think it's good news.

Just like the stage of adolescence wasn't adopted in society until around 1900, the stage of emerging adulthood is just coming in as the new normal. It's being adopted now. We are in the midst of the shift. "Emerging adulthood" is a relatively new term, coined by developmental psychologist Jeffrey Jensen Arnett, PhD in his work on the evolving social roles of young adults (he studied 18–25-year-olds, and later expanded his research to 18–29-year-olds).

Today we all accept adolescence as a distinct developmental stage of life even though we understand that there was a time when physical stature was the only measure of a kid's grown-upness, and that it wasn't so long ago when such thinking represented the cultural norm. Adolescence is no longer disputed as a real stage of development. The teen years carry through middle school and into high school. During these years kids change from children into something resembling their future adult selves. More than their bodies change. They become interested in relationships, dating, and sex. They are natural explorers, seeking out interesting experiences. Teens experiment and grow while their parents follow along as passengers on the journey, supervising and supporting. Teenagers need parents to keep them safe. The teen years offer supervised training in some of the ways of adulthood. Teens experiment with choices, and then return to home base to analyze, recharge, or accept the consequences of their behaviors. All the while, they absorb and grow and learn.

Emerging adulthood can reasonably be considered the second half of adolescence, the time for attaining psychological and emotional maturity, when one gradually takes on adult roles and responsibilities and becomes fully adult. If teens are student drivers with parents in the passenger seat, emerging adults are independently on the road, but don't have vast stores of experience. They still need to call home and ask for guidance when something unfamiliar happens out on the road of life.

Dr. Arnett began his work on young adult stage with interest in evolving social roles during the college years. A university professor, he saw twenty-something's progressing toward adult roles and responsibilities more slowly than had been the custom in previous generations. He noticed that his college students manifested a number of the behaviors one might associate more with teens than with adults. Dr. Arnett noted that the additional stage was used for self-exploration and examining the various possibilities in life. Emerging adults, as opposed to adolescents, have gained sufficient life experience and growth to be partially independent. Many move to college and live away from home. An emerging adult can make it in the world without direct supervision from older adults. They can work and earn income, fend for themselves, and generally go out and make a reasonable life for themselves. And yet, many developed countries favor a practice of extending adolescence by supporting young adults for many years while development continues.

The trend over the past couple of decades, in addition to encouraging more and more young people to enroll in colleges, has been that the extended stage of independence is no longer reserved for college students. Gradually, the stage of emerging adulthood is being adopted by the masses in developed countries. Twenty-somethings are delaying marriage, starting families later, getting more financial help, and living with their parents in record numbers. Perhaps this is because parents have resources to share and want to give their young adult children a leg up, or maybe it's because parents have taken note and realized that young people can benefit from more supervised experience. Whatever the case, society has gradually been changing toward recognizing that emerging adults are different than older adults. We keep them close a little longer, give them advice, and loan them money. They stay at home longer. We keep them under our wings.

The investigation into emerging adulthood, it turns out, expands beyond the sociology of parents helping their young adults longer and into neurobiology, where there is a growing body of knowledge indicating differences in the brains of emerging adults versus full-on adults. A surge in neuroscience research on brain development tells us brains aren't "adult" until the mid-twenties or later, around the same time when we see a natural acceptance of the responsibilities of full adulthood. Twenty-five year olds use better judgment, make fewer mistakes, and can be entrusted with greater responsibilities than younger adults. After twenty-five or so, growing up naturally seems to level off.

As the term implies, "emerging adults" are unfinished, still growing toward adulthood but not quite having arrived. They are one their way there. There is not a distinct line between childhood and adulthood; instead there is a gradual fading from one stage to the next, starting at puberty and concluding in the mid-twenties or beyond.

The changes in the brain that begin right around the time of puberty prepare teens for rapid learning. Their changing brains prep them for a new life, one they will create and take responsibility for. The connections in the brain are pruned back like hedgerows, being reshaped and made ready for tremendous new connections to form. During the overhaul from puberty to young adulthood, teens are ready to learn the social rules and culture that will carry them from their parents' homes and customs out into the adult world with their peers.

Late teens and young adults are big, strong, adult-sized creatures with a zest for learning that can leave them impatient to leave the nest and go out on their own. They feel ready, in part due to their thirst to gain new experiences and also out of a desire to create a life of their own choosing. The late teen/early twenties years create a window of opportunity during which most young people soak up knowledge, take on challenges and, feeling brave and capable, desire to leave the nest. The teen years are a time for a surge in physical development; the second half of the process of turning into an adult, emerging adulthood, is when social and psychological development can catch up.

Emerging adults take on a variety of new roles and responsibilities. These shifts may occur quickly en masse, for example when a graduate moves across the country alone to accept his first real career position, or the adult roles may come in small increments, when a student moves from his parents' house into an apartment across town near the school campus, but still visits his parents for family dinners a couple of nights each week. Emerging adulthood varies in length and complexity, depending on the individual and the family. There are still families releasing kids into full adulthood at age eighteen, while others are biting off adulthood in tiny pieces one at a time, a process that can go on for a decade or more.

This additional stage of emerging adulthood has many benefits, but has significant pitfalls as well. Since the stage was first established for students, it would thus end when young adults completed their education. There are problems with ending a stage of development in accordance with completing school. Some never graduate. Some never go to school at all. Some quit, deciding that school is not the right path. Not only do people drop out of colleges and universities, they extend time in school with graduate degrees, and they also may return for a second bachelor's degree, or a third, or a second master's, PhD, MD, or JD. Education is not one-size-fits-all, and a stage of life that revolves around education is often ill defined.

Emerging adulthood, changes in normal behavior of young adults today compared with the past, and the soaking up of identity and social learning all affect the way mental disorders disproportionately disable twenty-somethings. Emerging adults behave differently than their adult counterparts, and they are uniquely harmed by the shaping of their identities around disease and disability.

Emerging adulthood is all around us, and explains why previous generations are perplexed by millennials in the workplace. Why do they need so much support when they are in their mid-twenties? Even as the social scientists and the neuroscientists begin to converge on emerging adulthood, one important arena is behind the times: medical science. Medical professionals continue to draw the line between childhood and adulthood at the cultural standard, often eighteen. Psychiatry, tasked with addressing problems of behavior and mood, still generally holds the view that eighteen-year-olds are adults, just like their fifty-five-year-old parents. Mental health research is conducted on "adults" with an accepted age range of 18–65 in most research designs. Research results give average outcomes, and averages are applied to make treatment decisions for individuals. In psychiatry, such lagging ideology can be dangerous. Emerging adults are different in terms of the neurobiology of their brains.

Some of the problems we see currently with young adult mental health might be best understood through recognition of emerging adulthood as a stage. Rates of anxiety disorders are soaring in college populations, and many have assumed that kids arrive to college unprepared for its academic rigors. But perhaps the underlying change has more to do with adult readiness than academic readiness. College clinics are overrun, unable to meet the growing demand for mental health services to support their student populations. To solve the demand and meet the needs of young adults requires recognition of the cultural shift toward a distinct stage of emerging adulthood, leaving our youth more doe-eyed than ever before. They leave their families less grown-up than they once would have, arriving on campus without the experience of independence prior generations would have had.

To address the changing culture, colleges are welcoming parents into their orientations and even to advising sessions. Parents are checking grades. Professors are handholding. Even employers are changing workplace culture, using tools like employee report cards to give feedback in a format familiar to their young staff members.

The shift toward a distinct emerging adult stage has expanded outside individual families, and into the culture at large. The repercussions of these changes are not yet fully realized. But I think it's clear that they have an up side as well as a down side. There are unintended side effects as well as advantages. With more time to grow up, young adults make more thoughtful decisions once out on their own. They don't jump into marriage and family before they are ready, and they are free to leave bad jobs knowing they can turn to Mom and Dad for help if necessary. On the down side, shielded young people may gain fewer autonomous experiences from the school of life. If always protected, they can become poor problem-solvers, or even develop a fear of taking responsibility. That leaves more and more young people looking to pass the buck to the real grown-ups.

Sheltered young people start adulthood feeling unprepared. They get anxious facing the big, unknown world. They feel overwhelmed, and begin to look depressed. They lack the skills, and they give up easily. They end up in the psychiatric clinic, diagnosed with serious diseases according to a checklist that doesn't take their lack of experience into account, and are encouraged to step out of their newly adopted adult roles, and go into the sick role.

In this way, the societal addition of the emerging adulthood stage bears some responsibility for the growing trend of twenty-somethings struggling with mental health crises and disability.

For my high schooler at home, I'm glad he will have a little extra time to grow up. Once upon a time he could have gone out and gotten a factory job at fifteen, but I'm not sorry he'll be hanging on here for a while. These years to grow up will afford him more opportunities. He is likely to be wiser for the extra practice and additional guidance. But I'm also cautious about emerging adulthood and its side effects. I have told him that after eighteen, he is responsible for steering his own ship. I'll be here as a resource, but he should not expect me to clean up his messes or solve his problems. I have explained that things change after high school, and that it might feel uncomfortable. He might make mistakes and he might get scared, and that's all a normal part of growing up. I tell him he's going to be acquiring skills, and I'm going to try to stay out of the way while he learns.

CHAPTER 9

Why Do Parents Want
to Help, Anyway?

As noted in the previous chapter, I'm in favor of a dedicated stage of emerging adulthood for growth and maturity to continue. This additional stage provides a great many benefits to young adults and societies. Having a longer period of support allows young people to grow up and gain experience with emotional and financial backing from parents before being fully ready to take on independent responsibilities. Rather than leaving their families after puberty or at age eighteen to fend for themselves and learn from experience, emerging adults can continue to benefit from the structure, support, and wisdom of the family system much longer. They separate from the family wiser, with more skill development under their belts.

Emma lives with her parents as an emerging adult. She's turning twenty this month, and neither she nor her parents are ready for her to go out into the world just yet. Emma's mom tells me that she loves having her home, and is in no hurry to see her go out on her own.

"She really isn't ready. But that's fine. I want to give her plenty of time to find herself."

Emma volunteers with the Humane Society a few hours a week and has taken some art classes, but nothing for credit. She has considered a career as an artist, but doesn't know if she should enroll in actual credit courses, or just continue to produce drawings and paintings on her own to improve her skill. She hasn't yet decided if she believes additional education will help her have a successful future; if it's worth the investment of time and money. She also doesn't know if she can make it in the art world or if she needs to pursue some other way to make money while keeping art as her hobby. Right now, she just tries to live her life, be productive every day, gather information and gain skill, as she attempts to figure it out bit by bit. Art is an everyday pursuit. She helps her mom run the household to earn her keep while trying to figure out her own life.

Emma and her family feel pretty comfortable with this in-between stage. But not everyone agrees. Her mom's best friend is continually questioning the arrangement, suggesting that Emma is avoiding growing up because she is allowed to stay at home. The friend is such a vocal dissenter that Emma's mom has brought the issue into her session to ask me if I think she is making a terrible mistake. She quotes her friend's recent questions: "Why let her do this? Why let her stay with you rent-free? She is taking advantage. She'll be spoiled and dependent on you forever. Kick her out! Make her fend for herself. That will help her grow up. She's been with you almost two years since she graduated. She's twenty years old! Nothing good is going to come of this."

Yet Emma's mom defends the decision. She feels certain it's a better idea to let her daughter stay. "If I sent her out on her own, she would work at some useless job and immediately struggle to pay her bills. If she has to worry about making the rent, Emma's going to get trapped in some stupid job she hates. Stress is bad for your health, isn't it? What is she going to learn by wondering where her next meal is coming from? She would probably end up getting married too young, just to have help paying the bills. And that boyfriend of hers, he's not ready to get married either. Why rush them by putting the responsibility on them now? I've got a house with an extra room. She barely costs me anything. Why would I make her go? What's the point in leaving her to struggle? It's not going to help her."

Emma's mom is not alone in her philosophy about emerging adulthood. Just like the parents who save for college to try to pass along any advantages they can, others hold open space for their kids to benefit from family resources through their twenties as a way to increase opportunities for learning and growth. Parents, wanting the best for their children, agree to help them by allowing them to hang on to the family as long as they need. Doing so creates a space for maturation on many levels.

As families have more wealth (bigger houses, plenty of food, disposable income), we have become willing to share those resources with adult children longer. Contrast this to generations past when families just could not afford to let a young adult child stay around for free. It is one of the advantages of an affluent society to be able to pass on advantage to the next generation. We don't want to see them start over from the bottom to try to build a life from nothing. Not if we can help them.

Letting kids stay longer can have many advantages. Kids have time to complete higher education, grow up under supervision, explore various choices of career, and transform into less impulsive decision-makers. A dedicated emerging adulthood stage delays childbearing, so when our children finally choose to become parents they have the psychological and socioeconomic benefits of an older starting age. By starting later, many people then chose to have fewer children, decreasing the financial burdens associated with parenting and increasing the resources available to each child. And having parents help gives young people a leg up in the world, and increases socioeconomic success. Emerging adulthood pays socioeconomic progress forward to our children and their children. The emerging adulthood stage makes space for an exploration of the self that can thereby increase opportunity. Adding a period of emerging adulthood has been a positive change in quite a number of ways.

Parents offer support, understanding that their help gives their kids a chance at a better life. Parents help so kids can become educated and achieve some measure of emotional maturity before taking on the responsibilities of adult life. Parental support lets our kids level up before they even get started. This is why emerging adulthood has become a new standard stage, rather than something reserved for the rare few. However, the stage is only sometimes recognized for its true benefits. Detractors label emerging adulthood as a lazy self-pursuit and worry that we are raising a generation of helpless bums.

Parental help for emerging adults is not all about freeloading young people who refuse to act responsibly. What Emma's family friend fails to understand is that she *is* growing up. She spends her time productively, acquiring skills and toiling toward a vocation. She just happens to earn no income for the work. But many admirable vocations don't earn income. Take for example full-time parenting, art, or chairing a volunteer board. Learning to be a responsible, hardworking person does not necessarily equate straightforwardly to how many college credits one earns, or her annual salary. Growth is growth.

If Emma were truly stagnating, I would certainly not encourage her mom to continue the support. If she were behaving like an irresponsible teenager, defying Mom's rules, and refusing to take steps to further her own growth, by all means, kick her out and let her try something else. But Emma is thriving. She is taking responsibility. She is growing up and growing skills. She is moving forward toward her goals, not wasting away like an overgrown child. She is helpful to the household while developing her art style and skill.

When emerging adulthood works, it works the way it has for Emma. Parents provide support to help kids while they continue to grow and develop adult emotional and career skills. The young adults use the time and the resources to flourish, learn, and progress. They appreciate the opportunity, and they try to make the most of it. After two years, Emma has only come forward as a result of her parents' help, not slipped back. She is better today than she would have been without their help.

This is why parents help adult children: they want to give them a better life, and it's easy to offer the use of a bedroom in a house where the mortgage is paid or a bit of money when parents can spare it. Parents have built a solid base, and it doesn't take much effort to give some of what they have to benefit their kids. Parents think, "If I can offer her some help, why wouldn't I? It's not a big deal for me, but it makes a huge difference for my daughter when she's starting out."

Right now, I can only see one potential downside for someone like Emma, and I tell her mom as much. It has not yet been decided how the arrangement will come to an end. Emma won't have a graduation ceremony to serve as the line between dependency and independence. The period of extended support has no clearly demarcated endpoint, and sometimes it can go wrong before the final dismount. When parents begin helping so an emerging adult child can have a strong start, they end up confused and uncertain what to do if the child fails or falls off. And many fail.

They are doing fine for now, but they'll need some contingency plans in case they hit a rough patch. Just because Emma is thriving now, it doesn't mean their program will hold up if she stumbles off course.

CHAPTER 10

Parental Help Is Good, But Not for Everyone

Not every emerging adult welcomes parental support the way Emma did. Recently, I met with a surly graduating high school senior named Mark who arrived absolutely pissed at his parents for bringing him to see me. Mark was practically shackled and chained and dragged in for the appointment by his dad and mom because they were concerned about his bad attitude, his lack of a sense of responsibility, and just generally worried about his course of growth as a late-stage teen, set to leave home soon. He made it clear from the first few moments we met that he didn't want to talk to me. Mark walked into the room and immediately asked me if he could leave. He said unapologetically, "This is a waste."

Mark's parents sat down to tell me why they had brought him to meet with me. Before they began to speak, they breathed a giant exhausted sigh in unison. They looked weatherworn. While they took a moment and gathered their thoughts and I logged in to my laptop, Mark snorted and asked, "Well, if you don't have anything to say, can we just leave?" With this opener, Mark struck me as rude and abrasive.

By contrast, the two parents each spoke softly. Mark's parents said they had been divorced for ten years, but they co-parented together quite successfully most of the time. While their marriage had been full of differences, as parents, they were generally on the same page. And they were both worried about Mark. Mark had veered off course when he entered high school and puberty simultaneously. Since then, he was always going against the grain. He rejected every value his parents had taught him, especially their emphasis on education. He let his grades slip and said he no longer cared to strive to go to a good college. He might not want to go at all. In fact, he appeared to enjoy telling them that he didn't want to go to college. They believed he must know how upset it makes them to hear him say things like that, but he didn't temper his remarks at all. Maybe they could live with his differences of perspective, but what kind of person is cruel to his parents, upsetting them on purpose? So they finally decided to seek a psychiatric evaluation. Maybe he was having a breakdown that could explain his recent behavior.

Mark was routinely disrespectful and rude. He rejected his parents' wishes, even when those wishes were clearly in his best interest. The most obvious example was how he rejected the idea of college. He hadn't always rejected it, but certainly since he hit puberty, he had. Mark expressed his skepticism mildly at first, but over time had become firm in his assertions that he would not be going to college after high school. If the topic of higher education came up, Mark would blow up and bark that college was stupid.

Marks' parents said they had both put themselves through their college educations without much help. Education was of great value in their eyes. They had struggled to fund college and balance school with work, and it was hard. When they decided to start a family, they saved money for their kids' education, hoping to ensure better lives for their children. Even after they divorced, both parents contributed to the college funds. From the earliest lessons, they tried to teach both Mark and his sister about the value of getting an education. They explained how they had prepared by saving plenty of money.

As a family, not only did they expect an emerging adulthood stage for education, with assistance from parents, as a normal part of the growing up process, they prepared for it, talked about it, and developed a plan to fund it. Helping their kids would be good. It would bring opportunities. They imagined the kids would appreciate the help. After all, college is expensive and not all families pay for it. But since Mark got to high school, he seemed less and less inclined to follow his parents' values or wishes for him. He allowed his grades to slip so low that now he was barely passing, behavior flying in the face of their family values. The family also valued and respect for authority, especially teachers, and they pushed their kids to take personal responsibility for successes, failure, and mistakes. Mark got into trouble for missing class and rudeness with teachers. And lately, he talked about dropping out of high school. In every realm, he was irresponsible and disrespectful. At every turn he seemed to want to reject his parents' values.

He had told his parents he could get a good job working in construction without finishing school. Mark told them he hated school, and he hated his parents continued wish to have involvement in his life. Mark saw friends whose parents were much less involved or instructional. His friends got treated as adults by their parents. Not everyone was pressed to attend college. One close friend had already dropped out of high school to get a GED. Mark saw that as a potential path for himself, and his parents didn't understand why. They wanted to help him; why didn't he appreciate the opportunity? Or at least appreciate their willingness to help him?

They said they had brought him to talk to me hoping I could talk some sense into him, or else help them understand his motivations for resisting every wish the family had for his future. The family had reached a point where it was clear Mark was serious, and his parents wondered what was wrong with his thinking. They decided a professional might be able to explain it or repair him. With that, they stepped out of the room.

Parents out in the waiting room, Mark warmed to me just enough to tell me what he felt about the situation. He felt his parents ought to adjust their outdated views and let him pave his own way in life. He felt he was a man; that his parents should back off and let him run his life on his own terms. He didn't understand why they felt the need to have a hand in his future. He said he didn't see any reason for his parents to worry about him or try to be so involved in his life. He just wanted to be an adult and have them leave him be. He knew he could handle his life his way, and he felt disrespected by his parents' heavy-handed involvement.

Mark confirmed his parents' claim that he hated school, and he wanted to drop out. His parents often lectured him about why school was important for his future, why he needed as much education as possible. He questioned why they wanted him to graduate high school, and why they believed attending additional school was important. To him, his parents were controlling, and they were determined to make him into a person who would be just exactly like them. He felt his life was his own to live, on his own terms. If he was fed up with school and didn't want to be a student until he was thirty-five, he thought his parents should respect his choice and butt out. Instead, they pushed and pushed for Mark to be a carbon copy of everyone else in the family.

I asked him, "Okay, but don't you think your parents are just trying to help? Isn't this just what parents do?" I assumed they wanted what they believed was in his best interest, because that is what parents often want to achieve when they push teens or young adults toward a specific course. Whether kids want to accept that help may be their own choice, but parents want to help anyway.

I couldn't imagine I would talk Mark out of his perspective, but I didn't think his parents were trying to be controlling. As a parent, I agreed with saving for college and encouraging education. Offering help to our young adult children, so they can have opportunities and create a stronger platform to launch from, should feel like something positive. Loving parents have often saved for years to provide such assistance. We want to share our material successes with our kids, and share our accumulated wisdom as well. We want them to have a chance to express their talents instead of just struggle to survive month by month.

When we can pay tuition, or assist our kids in renting or buying an apartment or a home, we receive all the rewards that come with giving and loving our children. This kind of parenting is not intended to be controlling. We are trying to help them by doing these things. Especially during the very important time of transition away from the nuclear family, we parents feel the profound importance our love and support can have in the lives of our children going forward.

Parents help to offer the promise of a better life to children, a life of more stability and less struggle. But does it work? When we keep kids dependent longer, when we offer them not only an adolescence, but an emerging adulthood as well, does it help them? Sitting there with Mark, trying to accept his point of view and see the validity in what he was saying, I had to consider how it felt to have your parents plot out a course for your young adult years and refuse to listen when told the plan was a poor fit.

By suggesting to Mark that his parents probably wanted to improve his future, I essentially ended our alliance. He looked immediately annoyed. He didn't need another adult siding with his parents, and so he was finished talking to me. He insisted it was time for him to leave.

At the end of my day, I left with Mark on my mind. His point of view about his parents made me wonder what advice I should give. Were his parents wrong? Were they invading into his space by planning and pushing for the future they envisioned for him? Maybe I was doing the same thing, and maybe it would mess up my kids.

Mark's parents scheduled a follow-up session for him on the way out, but when the day of the appointment came, he refused to get in the car with his parents. He told them there was nothing I could do for him. So his parents came to the session without him. They asked if we could use the time to discuss what the next steps might be for Mark. They could see that he wasn't interested in seeking help for himself. He didn't hold the opinion that he had a problem he needed to fix. And he didn't want to hear anyone suggest he might not be right. So what could they do now?

Still confused about who was right and who was wrong, I simply listened to them explain the family dynamic in further detail. They were at a breaking point, and they needed to decide whether to continue on the path they had planned and push Mark toward college, or give in and let him take a job instead. I sat there pondering about what I should advise.

In the session, the parents contrasted the situation with Mark with their older daughter, Katie. Katie was soon to graduate from Rice

University. She had always adopted the values her parents set forth, and it was paying off for her. She got a scholarship to a prestigious school, and she worked in two different impressive internships. She considered a variety of fields, but when her parents told her they believed she belonged in STEM, she trusted them. Placing her education first, trusting her parents' advice, and respecting authority figures had helped Katie land a job in the biomedical engineering field straight out of school. In other words, Mark's parents had seen their values and their approach to parenting work with Katie. With help from parents, Katie had been able to go to a better school than either of her parents had done. She was able to accept an unpaid internship that afforded priceless work experience instead of taking a paid position (which would have been her only choice if parents hadn't paid the bills while she worked unpaid).

Katie had the opportunity to use her talents and fully realize her potential. And she only had this opportunity because of the hard work and sacrifices her parents made on her behalf. Their advice and guidance led her toward worthwhile goals, and their savings helped pay the way. She followed in her parents' footsteps, and was then able to move toward a better future. This was exactly what they had intended with their support and advice: greater opportunities and a chance at a better life for their children.

These parents made a lot of sacrifices, and saw them pay off as envisioned for their daughter. They watched friends and family members make many of the same choices for their children, with similarly positive results. Parental support could make a dramatic difference in the lives of young people. They felt it intuitively, and they saw it all around them in practice. It had never occurred to them that one of their children would reject the chance at an education, or the advice of successful, experienced parents. Mark was making things more difficult than necessary by refusing to follow the path laid out for him. Without a formal education, he would earn less and work harder. He might be sentencing himself to a life of hard work for little payoff. Why would he reject the easier path when he had watched it work so perfectly for his sister? Couldn't he see how their assistance had fueled Katie's progress all along the way?

By then, I knew what I should say. I pointed out how their help had improved things for Katie. She had outstanding opportunities because she loved school and trusted her parents' advice. I could see why all those years of shaping values and saving money could pay off in the end. But Mark had a right to refuse to walk through the door his parents could open, and if that was the choice he was making, his parents would have to accept it. In other words, their help was a wonderful gift, but not every child was going to agree to receive it. I advised them to leave the college money in the fund for a few years and see if Mark changed his mind, but not to continue to wrestle with him over the issue. If he did have any spark of interest in college, arguing over the issue was going to push him away further. And they had to consider the possibility that perhaps Mark was right. Maybe he knew himself and was trusting his own intuitions. Maybe he was better off going straight into the workforce than choosing the route of higher education. Maybe he wouldn't like the careers available to him without education, or maybe he would excel. Who knew? The important thing was that the parents had given him the option to choose with all of their hard work and advanced planning. And now they were reaching the stage where they would have to let go. Mark was beginning to carve out his own path, and they would have to respect his wishes for now.

CHAPTER 11

Enabling, Resentment, and Getting Stuck along with Your Kid

amilies often try to facilitate their kids' futures like Katie and Mark's parents described doing in the last chapter. They plan ahead and steer kids toward worthwhile goals. They save money for the future, and teach kids that education is the ticket to a good life. Or if not education, parents push some value set: take over the family business, go into military service, or otherwise follow in the footsteps of friends and family who know what's best. Parents attempt to set it all up for their kids. But helpful parents can find themselves enabling negative behavior instead of helping.

Katie benefitted fully from her parents assistance. She showed why parental help gives people an advantage. However, like Katie's little brother Mark, some teens and young adults don't accept the path their parents have laid out for them. Amber was such a teen. At first she looked like she was headed along the road her parents had planned. She started community college to complete two years of basics, and had a plan to transfer to a four-year university. But

Amber didn't like college and wasn't very successful at it. Poor grades diminished her self-esteem, and she quit going to classes. She didn't get through her community college basics as planned, and transferring to a four-year college became an unlikely prospect. She quit school and she quit functioning. She felt a little down, nervous, unfocused, and unmotivated. She decided the symptoms meant she suffered from Attention Deficit Disorder. She went to counseling for a while to learn tips for getting organized, and pretty quickly quit the counseling too. She was urged to find a job and didn't. She quit every active pursuit, and ultimately parked herself at home.

Like many families in this position, Amber's parents began by giving her time to re-group. However, rest and time led to complete inertia.

After waiting too long to see progress where there was none, Amber's parents found themselves stuck in the quagmire with her. They couldn't run her life, but she couldn't run it either. They had expected her to graduate from college and start a career. When she proved unable to take that route, her parents were uncertain what to say. They felt trapped right along with her. They were in a position they did not enjoy, and also did not know how to remedy. How do parents help an adult child who has gone off the path when they don't know what she can or will reasonably do to get her life back in order? Their suggestions and directions failed to help in the first place, so what help would more parental suggestions provide now? And what was Amber capable of successfully doing for herself, anyway? Maybe she was unable to follow any plans they set forth. They had placed themselves in the role of running Amber's life, and when their plans didn't pan out, Amber had already proven she wasn't qualified to simply take the reins and run her life herself.

Having realized it was time to change strategy, Amber's parents had long since stopped trying to manage her life for her. They gave her time, and backed away from the day-to-day management of her goings-on, hoping to see Amber grow up and take over for herself. She didn't budge. She didn't grow. She didn't function. Nothing changed at all. As time plodded forward, her parents developed a steadily growing sense of frustration. The frustration fermented into resentment. They didn't want to be the answer for Amber's problems. She had had plenty of time to grow up, and they wanted her to step out into the world and make a life for herself outside the family home. They didn't want to have to provide for her anymore, financially or emotionally. They didn't want to be stuck with Amber, an overgrown dependent child, forever.

Although parents may take pleasure in helping kids as they transition out from the family, sometimes helping does not feel rewarding anymore. Parenting is particularly displeasing when plans fail to work out. Parents set out to assist, they pay tuition and rent or they help solve pressing problems, but when the plans fail to produce fruit, it can become unclear who is responsible for picking up the pieces and deciding what happens next. Sometimes, parents end up feeling frustrated, used, and resentful. Resentments loom large when flailing young adults continue to look to befuddled parents for answers to life's questions.

Resentful feelings are not the natural result of helping emerging adults sprout wings and fly. Resentment is not a universal part of the process. Amber's parents would have felt differently if she were thriving. True help yields feelings of warmth and positivity. Resentment, by contrast, often signifies that something has gone wrong. Parents begin to feel resentful when they find themselves working harder toward their kids' futures than the kids are working. Parents feel resentful when they are stuck holding the bag for an adult child who is off track and shows few signs of returning to a healthy, productive life. The presence of resentment signifies an immediate need to shift course.

In contrast to the warm, positive feeling brought by healthy support, resentment is often brought on by enabling. Enabling is a psychological term frequently used in the addiction recovery community, and it specifically means helping someone in the wrong way, so that they remain unhealthy. Enabling is covering up for a teen's misdemeanors, only to have them grow into felonies in adulthood. Enabling is buying a child a brand new car so she will feel better after wrecking the first one. Enabling is cleaning up after messes and making excuses. Enabling prolongs and increases unhealthy behavior. When parents enable unhealthy young adult behavior, it may happen in a number of domains, but it almost always results in the same negative feelings and relationship consequences. Enabling causes parents to feel angry, disappointed, and bitter. In the case of young adults who fail to launch from the family, enabling is parenting and providing for them as if they were still age ten or fifteen. Parents don't set out to enable problem behavior; they do it when they are out of ideas and operating from default habits after years of parenting.

The only hint for many parents that their help is problematic lies in the presence of inner negative feelings. Parents feel excitement and enthusiasm at the prospect of helping kids start out in adult life. If parents offer help and their child never actually starts as planned, negative emotions start to emerge. Parents may pay tuition for their child to go to school, or rent to move out. When the adult child comes back to parents with failing grades or asking for rent money it was her job to cover, writing that check doesn't feel so fulfilling anymore.

Along with resentment, Amber's parents felt other negative emotions, most prominently guilt. They felt guilty for pushing her in what was later obviously the wrong direction. They felt guilty for not knowing what to do after the plans fell apart. And increasingly with time, they felt guilty for just wanting her out of the house; for being tired of dealing with her problems to no avail. It was the guilt that kept them trapped in the enabling loop with Amber. It felt terrible to want your daughter to just go away.

Recognizing the presence of negative feelings like resentment and guilt can be an excellent tool for parents to identify when they have crossed over from loving assistance into unhealthy enabling of problem behavior. When it doesn't feel good, it isn't good. During the times when parents offer appropriate help, such resentful feelings are not the pervasive ones. Supportive parents feel warm, connected, and hopeful. It is only when the assistance begins to encourage dysfunctional coping that unpleasant feelings rise.

Sometimes parents become confused on this point. They set out to be helpful to kids, and they held romanticized notions of how wonderfully smooth the transition to adulthood would then be. When things take a bad turn, parents can't quite identify what they should do. Supporting kids during the college (or college equivalent) years is sometimes what parents want to do.

If you are enabling your adult child as the parent, the feelings of resentment are trying to clue you in and tell you to stop.

Identifying enabling is only the first step. In the next chapter, I explore practical advice to help parents who feel stuck in situations that leave them resentful and frustrated.

PART 3

CHAPTER 12

Structure Is Key

U p to this point, we have been defining the problems that lead to emerging adults getting stuck at home. From here until the end of this book, there will be more discussion of solutions. And the first solution is structure.

When Amber dropped out of college and didn't take the reins of her life, her parents found themselves frustrated and resentful at being stuck with the responsibility. Amber ended up back home, and her parents were left with the burden of parenting her again and taking care of her like a child, even though she was an adult. In the previous chapter, we discussed how Amber's parents could identify that the situation was unhealthy: they could recognize that the resentments they felt were cues that things needed to change. They recognized the cues, but still had to come up with a plan for change.

So then what are Amber's parents, or other parents whose kids are sinking into the quicksand and becoming stuck, to do? If you're this parent, what can you do? A parent could talk to Amber about getting out and looking for work, or returning to school and improving her grades, but would Amber improve after a strong talking to? They could punish her, but would she learn or grow as a result? They could kick her out of their house, put her out on the street, but then how would that help her? How would they be supporting her growth? It can be hard for parents stuck with a stuck young adult to understand how to help her. Compounding matters further, kids like Amber have problems their parents often don't fully understand. Why is she having so much trouble in the first place? Is she sick? Does she need medical or psychological treatment? Parents aren't sure how to comprehend the problem, and therefore are at a loss as to the best solution. In truth, Amber not making it through college is not the primary issue. Plenty of people choose to forego higher education, but most of them don't end up stuck and lost, relying on their parents. To comprehend the true roots of the problem, it helps to rewind and go back to where getting stuck begins.

When parents set out to assist young adult children with education or in other ways help with the launch process, too often they do so without a clear blueprint for where they are trying to go. Amber's parents saved for college and planned to pay tuition and expenses for a few years, but they didn't have much more planned for the future. They imagined her education would unlock the next set of doors. They imagined a best-case scenario, with only minimal contingency planning. If Amber didn't complete an education, her parents probably expected her to go out and begin working. They probably didn't consider the possibility that she would follow neither path, and instead end up back at home doing nothing much at all.

In-case-of-failure planning is often not part of the blueprint parents lay out for their children's assisted launch. They prepared for a different future than the one they are living out; a simpler one where things would go smoothly. But how often does it really go so well? Parents send kids off to college with a clear expectation that things will go well, but things often go wrong, and then families are caught without a contingency plan. What happens when little Johnny starts smoking marijuana and missing classes? What happens when Suzie fails half her coursework? Many families have not considered what will happen if things fall apart in their child's process of leaving home.

Sure, nobody wants to imagine their kid failing at adulthood. Planning for failure would have been more advisable than having no plan at all. Amber's parents have found themselves distressed and emotionally strained, and trying to formulate a strategy in a state of turmoil. That's difficult to do. Supporting young adult children while they transition away from the family home is unlike supervising and caring for a child or teen that lives with you. Families in this position cannot cue from prior experience, because this new situation doesn't follow the same rules. Adult children are not blindly obedient, and punishing them to ensure their compliance stops working when kids enter the stage of young adulthood, especially when they are lost and no longer functioning. It's hard to get any traction by restricting a twenty-year-old from going out with friends when she has no money and nowhere to go anyway, especially since her friends are busy working and going to school.

Parents offering support would do well to think through all the ways plans get off track, and decide in advance what the rules of support will be if things don't go as initially planned. Amber's family would be in better shape today, and Amber would be in better shape, had they done a little bit of advance planning for her to struggle or fail. Families who imagine the variety of ways the launch can fail are then able to decide what will happen if a child comes back home unexpectedly.

Unfortunately, because the emerging adult stage is a fairly new invention, parents often enter it without a clue as to what commonly goes wrong or what needs to happen to ensure a smooth adjustment. Often parents are naive about the problems families face when supporting a young adult, and their friends and neighbors are reluctant to share their own knowledge gained through failures and mistakes, because family mistakes at this stage are handled as private matters. Friends and family aren't calling one another up on the telephone to say, "Amber failed out of college and now she sits up in her room refusing to look for a job. I know this happened to your daughter, too. How did you handle it?" These failures are embarrassing. And not only that, parents have a very real sense that discussing an adult child's problems with anyone else is a betrayal of trust. Perhaps it is. Our kids don't want us telling everyone we know that they are depressed or stressed or unorganized. They don't want to hear us gossiping about their problems with friends and neighbors to make ourselves feel better.

However, if parents had the benefit of hearing from those who have failed and fallen before them, we would all be much better equipped when it happens. Most experienced parents would warn you to have a clear structure in place before offering parental support to an emerging adult child. Decide under what circumstances you can offer money or any other type of assistance, and what you expect from your young adult while you are giving support. Be flexible, not rigid. You may begin by saying you expects A's in college in exchange for your support, and later realize that your child's best work doesn't produce an A in a tough chemical engineering program. It's okay to change course, but still better to sketch out a structure to follow in the beginning.

Equally important is to share this plan in depth with your child. If you have expectations and you want to make agreements with your young adult, to define the terms for support and lay out your expectations, she needs to know precisely what you are thinking and planning in advance of her first mistake.

- What will you pay for? What will you refuse to pay for?

- When will you pay?

- How will you pay?

- What if the assistance you offer doesn't lead to the successes you had in mind?

- Does your child need to pass classes? Pay half the rent? Have a part-time or a full-time job?

- Are you willing to continue to fund school if your child chooses to transfer out of accounting and into a dedicated school for music, theater, or art?

- Can your child move back home? Under what circumstances? For how long? Will she need to pay rent if she lives at home?

- Will there be conditions and stipulations to your help? Will those change if she takes time off from school for a gap year? Or drops out?

- Are you available to give your son advice every day? If not every day, how often and about what?

- Will you pay for rent on an apartment he shares with his girlfriend? Or his boyfriend?

- What if he decides to get married while you're still supporting him financially? Will you still sign the checks then? For how long and under what circumstances?

- What about an unplanned pregnancy? How would you be willing to help then?

- What if your child has a medical crisis?

- A substance use or addiction crisis?

- An abusive partner?

When creating a structured plan for your support, it's important to stop and think about what can predictably go wrong for your child during your period of assistance. That means considering both academic or work factors, and stage of life growth factors. Ask other parents what went wrong for them or their kids' friends. What if you offer to pay for college but he follows the seven-year plan? What if you put her up in an apartment and pay the first few months rent to help her get started, and then she quits her job and can't pay her rent when she has agreed to take it over? Can she expect you to pay the rent until she finds a new job? Should she consult you before deciding to quit? What if he puts $1000 on your credit card for unneeded clothes? Will that change the arrangement? What if your relationship with the young adult you are supporting becomes strained? Will you continue to support a young adult son or daughter who refuses to return your phone calls for months on end or shouts at you and calls you a worthless asshole?

Arrangements for financial support, housing, covering health insurance or car insurance all require a precise understanding between parent and adult child, not only of how things will go if it works out well, but also what will change if things get complicated or messy or ugly. Since many things can go wrong, it's often best to write out a plan in the form of a contract, and have all involved parties sign it when they agree.

A young adult child with a history of mild autism needs a different plan than a neurotypical child with no history of problems. During emerging adulthood, each person requires a tailor made program designed to support his specific strengths and minimize his weaknesses where possible.

Structuring a plan in advance helps you pre-think your response to problems long before you're facing them. But that's not all. Informing kids what's at stake if they fail classes or quit jobs can help them make better choices and avoid a crisis in the first place.

CHAPTER 13

Get Control with a Plan

F or many families reading this book, the advice in the previous chapter comes too late. Maybe your family had a clearly mapped out Plan A, but didn't have Plan B, C, or D for contingencies when something went awry. You began the period of support for your emerging adult child, probably to help him or her with education, and your arrangement lacked adequate alternative pathways when the train went off the tracks. Like so many parents, you began supporting your adult child, and when he ran off course with his life fully derailed, no one knew quite what to do next. And then it's hard to think reasonably through the planning under the stress that ensues.

Recall Amber from the previous two chapters. She quit college and her parents were stuck with her, as she became stuck in life. While her parents might look back in retrospect and realize that contingency planning would have been wise, after she's home as a college dropout without a job, they cannot rewind the clock. So what do they do now? What do you do if this is your situation?

After Amber returns home, having decided that college is not in her future, her parents cannot accept her back with a vague, open-ended arrangement. They'll need structure and organization because Amber cannot muster the willpower to find her way without structure. Amber's lack of direction or internal structure is commonplace for a young adult who has returned home unexpectedly. She returned home after an unsuccessful Plan A, and then she could not formulate any kind of Plan B for herself. She had no skills or experience for plotting her life plans. Let's consider why.

The only life Amber had experienced at home was being in the child role. She went off to start school as a teen, and returned very soon afterward with the expectation from her parents and society that she was now an adult. But Amber has no real experience being an adult. Her parents had always taken care of her needs, providing food, clothing, and shelter every moment of her life until she left for school. As a kid and later a teen, she was expected to attend school, complete homework, and follow rules. She was good at following orders, or else she was punished as a child. Occasionally, she might have failed to follow rules and gotten grounded. Her parents might have gotten annoyed with her, but they still continued to take care of her. This is the familiar world Amber imagines she is returning to, and she has no real reason to expect otherwise. Amber's inability to behave in an adult way is not evident to her parents, though.

Consider their perspective. They see her as a young adult. She has reached the legal age of adulthood, and spent a period of time living away from home. She meets the definition of an adult in their views. And this sets the family up for mismatched expectations and tons of conflict. They expect her to take some responsibility, maybe get a job, formulate a plan to move out or at least assist with the household expenses. They expect her to take on the standard roles of an adult because she is one. Adults manage their own affairs, pay their own way, take responsibility, and clean up their own messes.

These adult roles are ones Amber has never had, yet she is expected to take them on the moment she returns home. Her parents paid her way when she was a child. They even supported her while she was attending college. They cleaned up her messes until now, too. They were always the responsible, accountable ones. Amber doesn't yet know how to function independently. She doesn't know how to work and pay bills. She has never done these things. At first, she may be confused about what is expected. Even as it becomes clearer, she may not be comfortable taking it on. She may try to hand the baton back to her mom and dad.

Amber is faced with the familiar experience of disappointing her parents, and maybe even imagines getting grounded for refusing to get a job. All the while, though, she may be resting assured deep down that they will take care of her. They always have. Or, perhaps she knows her parents won't tolerate child-like behavior, and maybe it's obvious that failing to act like an adult means more than disappointing her parents. But when she imagines going out and facing an unknown adult world, a world in which she is expected to fend for herself, she may decide that disappointing her parents is an easier road to go down. She can accept the familiar unpleasantness of angry parents. She prefers the familiar to the scary unknown out in the real adult world. She'll prefer to take the easy path if she can.

Left with the choice of facing an unknown adult world, or hiding at home and disappointing her parents, which route do you think she would choose? Which would you choose in her shoes?

With only a loose understanding of the plan for support, or the expectations of her parents, or most importantly the consequences of inactivity (she isn't likely to understand how her failure affects her future), chances are that Amber will stay hidden upstairs way too long. She may prefer to disappoint her parents than take on the big, scary grown up world for the first time, feeling afraid and alone. Adulthood is out there, a nebulous world of work and stress and strain that she only knows about intellectually. Her bedroom is a place she understands, and while staying in bed might make her feel ashamed and frustrated, it's easier to stay than to muster the courage to go out in the world and take a risk on the unknown. But what might happen if her parents laid out Plans B, C, and D after the first plan tanked?

Having some alternative to Plan A in her mind can help Amber start to pull herself together faster.

Maybe Plan B says find a full-time job within one month, pay $400 per month to parents in rent, take over the car insurance expenses and cell phone payments, and (assuming she can follow all of the basic house rules for respect, cleanliness, and common courtesy) she can stay home for a full year. Plan C might address some "what if's." What if she cannot find full-time work, but part-time is available? Maybe then she would be expected to make up additional hours equivalent to full-time by volunteering for a worthy cause, providing babysitting services for younger siblings, or doing service work at the church or temple. Plan D might read, "Or we will give you $1500 to get started, move you into an apartment, and wish you good luck starting out on your own."

For some families, suggestions like the B, C, and D above are too expensive, or out of line with their values. Some families wouldn't offer any help, and others need help at the family business. There is no one size fits all for an adult life.

There are many alternatives to these plans, and the list a family could outline might reach much further down into the alphabet. But the important point is that dependent emerging adults need first to see they have options, next to make reasoned/responsible choices, and then finally be expected to be accountable for the outcomes of their decisions in a way that helps them grow.

Options. Choices. Outcomes.

They won't do well to expect parents to take care of them as if they are children, but to change course (or get on course in the first place) requires that parents add structure to the planning. Once they become stuck, emerging adults lack the life experience to control their anxiety and shame, and also find the energy to create the necessary order in their own lives. They often lack the life experience to see the whole picture or find solutions.

When things get off track, it is time to write out the contract you will soon wish you had prepared earlier. Writing down what expectations and arrangements you hold for your adult child is key to gaining control after the support for your young adult has gotten messy and off track.

If your adult child was offered a period of support to work toward a goal, let's say completing a six-month long computer coding certificate program, and he drops out of the program, what is your next move? Whether you agreed to help with education, or sponsor your artist while she works on her first art show, or help finance a move to a new city, what comes next if then plan unravels? No matter what was planned or what has gone wrong, the next step is the same: sit down and create a clearly structured plan for the next phase.

Make a plan. Create a contract.

When adults are receiving support, explicit contracts get everyone on the same page. For children and adolescents, there is a shared social contract, defined by the larger society. We know the rules. But for adults? Those rules we each define ourselves. So we need to spell them out to ensure everyone is working from the same playbook.

This was true when your child set out to complete college, try her hand at a first job, or attend a training program, and had your involvement and financial assistance. It's also true when he completes his coding program, but moves home to look for a job. What if she never finds one? When things fail to work out as planned and the parent is the one left holding the bag, it's time to step back and plan.

It's time to outline a new arrangement. What are parents willing to offer now that things have changed? Have you been paying the rent under the prior arrangement? Is the rent still going to be paid? If yes, for how long? If no, will you need to break a lease? How long will the next phase of support (assuming there will be one) last? What are the expectations of the adult child? Are there any behaviors that would stop parents from helping? (Before you discount the need for this one, consider drug use, underage drinking, bringing home strangers for sexual soirees, or destroying property in a fit of rage.) Are there any deal breakers?

No matter the situation or previous arrangement, when an offer of support has gone off the rails, the next step is to make a new plan and write it down. When families wing it, they are at risk of ending up off course again.

CHAPTER 14

What Happens When
Emerging Adults Are Sick?

U p to this point in this section, we have focused on creating and implementing a structured support plan for a mostly healthy adult child. It is important to think about how to address a stuck emerging adult who is healthy and capable, but this is a book about kids who are (or appear to be) sick. What happens when you are the parent of an adult child who is obviously not healthy? What happens when your child is clearly having panic attacks every day? When he is majorly depressed? When she is hooked on dangerous street drugs? It's easy to imagine kicking an able-bodied yet slightly lazy adult child out of the house and saying, "Go figure it out," but many times the train derails because something is truly wrong. How do parents make decisions when kids are unable to function as healthy adults?

Mental health problems in young adulthood can take many forms. The field of mental health covers problems with thoughts, feelings, behaviors, or functioning day to day. Unwanted or unpleasant thoughts include obsessions (for example fear of germs), irrational beliefs (seeing "signs" all around that someone is following you) or intrusive thoughts (awful or shameful images or words that pop into the mind unwanted). Feeling states can cause distress, such as pervasive sadness or non-stop fear. Behavior problems can include uncontrolled anger, constant avoidance, risk taking, or the use of substances. And finally, functional problems may include not attending work or school, and those can be caused by problem thoughts, feelings, or behaviors; or they can be separate issues altogether.

Key point worth repeating: functional problems may be caused by feelings, thoughts, or behaviors, or they may be separate issues all together.

When a mental or behavioral health problem develops, it can take time for patients and families to understand and manage it. A crisis hits, and confusion ensues. It takes a while to get everything to stop spinning, and then settle back into a state of calm. Commonly, daily functioning takes a back seat during the crisis management stage of treatment for a mental health condition. Safety takes precedence over everything else. It is when the crisis has ended that addressing the ability to function each day returns to the forefront again. However, families can look up from the chaos and find themselves overwhelmed as they think about how to get life back on track.

Elena had a long history of anxiety and depression, and when she went out of state for college she immediately began to decline into a full-fledged crisis. It wasn't a case of mild distress or occasional crying; Elena spiraled down into the depths of depression until she found herself hopeless and downright suicidal. She tried to hold on and stay in school. When she couldn't take it anymore, she downed a bottle of Tylenol with a chaser of vodka and ended up spending two weeks in the psychiatric hospital. Her university placed her on medical leave. Elena returned home to stay with her parents after the suicide attempt because she, her parents, and the university all agreed she was not safe to stay on campus so far from home when at risk of suicide.

Jack was a thriving college student and a moderate drinker when he began having bouts of abdominal pain. He ended up spending six weeks on the general medical floor of a local hospital and was diagnosed with a rare but serious liver impairment. It was bad news, life-changing. Rather than a normal life, he would face chronic pain, expensive medical treatments, and a life of chronic health problems. He dropped out of his university and moved home. The illness would necessitate treatments for the rest of his life, and he would be required to follow a strict diet and never consume a drop of alcohol again. He would suffer from chronic fatigue and general weakness, but otherwise be able to function.

Courtney started partying with pills during high school. She and her friends would get together and spread out whatever pills they could gather from their parents' medicine cabinets. They would take different combinations. Courtney learned that she liked Vicodin and, if she could get it, she liked OxyContin even more. She found someone at school to purchase pills from on a regular basis, and she developed a full-fledged addiction to painkillers. When the pills were in short supply and she still needed a fix, she turned to heroin, first smoked and then eventually used intravenously. A year after moving out on her own, she was found unresponsive and rushed to the hospital for an overdose. Her parents sent her to rehab, and moved her things back into her old bedroom. She wouldn't be safe to live on her own for a long time.

Elena, Jack, and Courtney all suffered a serious health crisis and as a result stagnated in their move toward adulthood. Rather than completing college or venturing into the adult world of work, each of them was forced to put their plans on hold and focus on their health instead. Their parents had to step back into their lives and help them. And while their parents wouldn't necessarily want them to get stuck back in a child role, they had to first get to a point of safety and stability. Each one needed support, and help from the family. These adult kids aren't like the immature or lazy stereotypes of young adults who go back to live with their parents. They are each seriously ill. Without help from their families, none of them would have been able to get the medical care they needed or support themselves for quite a long while. They all needed to return home and accept help, just as they would have done if their illness was cancer or diabetes. But depression, chronic diseases causing hidden pain or fatigue, and addiction are health problems that present some unique challenges compared with cancer and diabetes.

For one, cancer and diabetes most commonly reach a point of clear medical stability. After the initial crisis, the clinical picture takes shape, giving patients and families specific details for a prognosis. The cancer requires ten weeks of chemo, and then hopefully goes into remission. The diabetic's blood sugars come under regular control. Depression, on the other hand, takes a disorderly course, has a constant risk of relapse, and there is no blood test (at this time) to track its progression. Likewise, fatigue and addiction are difficult to measure. People with mental illnesses, addictions, or chronic fatigue or pain may not reach a point of stability or wellness. They may remain in a state of distress for a long time, without a straightforward path out of their suffering. Or, even if they are biologically improving, without tests and scans to reassure them, they live in constant fear of their diseases.

Elena, Jack, and Courtney may not exactly go into remission. They won't rest assured that they are achieving reliable stability, and neither will their parents. And it is in this limbo between health and sickness that they may be at risk of relinquishing adulthood and going straight back into childhood to stay, dragging their parents along for the ride.

Just as a healthy young adult who fails out of college might go back to bed, a sick adult child is likely (probably more likely) to go upstairs, climb under the covers, and refuse to come out for a very long time rather than face starting over with a serious disease. At first, seeking the familiar comforts of childhood after a downturn in health makes sense. A big crisis brings a major shift in the life plan. One needs to grieve. Adjusting to the new normal takes time. "I'm sick. I'm tired. My life is not going to be the same." But too commonly, that grief has no end. It can feel as though building a full life is pointless, not worth the effort when looking down the road and seeing relapses and exacerbations. A life of sickness is a tiresome prospect.

These young folks, facing the terrible reality that their lives just took a major detour, aren't likely to emerge from bed ready to take on the world on their own. They'll need a push. Remember, these kids were barely out of the gate from childhood, and so never really got on their feet as adults. They don't know a life of responsible independence. They don't have careers or well developed adult identities. They have eighteen years of experience being dutiful children, and now a brief experience with crisis and bad news. If adulthood is on the horizon, getting there won't happen automatically. Their parents must offer a strategic nudge to get them going.

Nudging a sick emerging adult forward takes courage and a leap of faith on the part of a parent. Having a sick young adult child leaves parents feeling uncertain about whether it's safe or healthy to enforce expectations. Parents worry that they will ask too much and push the adult child further into crisis. However, even during a time of crisis, creating structure and spelling out expectations are vital steps toward ensuring the best possible outcome.

If Jack's parents don't push him to do anything, his dreams and plans for the future may slip away entirely rather than change form. He could grow to see himself as incapable, cursed, or simply unwilling. With a safe family to retreat into, he may sink into hopelessness and just let his parents take over. Elena may decide that depression robs her of a normal life, and that things will never be any different. She may go back to bed and hide from adulthood. Courtney may believe herself fragile in her recovery, unable to take risks for fear of relapse. She may be too afraid to get a job or return to society, thinking she cannot both stay clean and have a normal life.

But Jack, Elena, and Courtney have a chance to rebuild their lives and thrive in the future. Myriad adults cope with illnesses and still have full lives, complete with career, independence, and a wide circle of loving people around them. People with chronic illnesses can still have meaningful lives, fulfilling occupations, relationships and families of their own, and independence. Their lives are not over, even with the health problems they each face. Their sickness does not directly translate to disability. Even very sick people can move out of their parents' homes eventually to go out and create the lives they want. Plenty of people struggle with chronic illnesses, but they don't necessarily stop living.

If Elena were your adult child, and she came home from college after a suicide attempt, you would need a structured plan for how you would assist her. If you don't decide on a plan, your adult child may end up crawling into bed and never getting out, crippling her chances of a full recovery. Likewise, if you found out your daughter has been shooting up heroin, your job will be the same. The difference in these situations is not your role; when an adult child comes back to the family for assistance, the parents' role is universally to create structure, enforce the expectations that are set, and communicate well with the adult child. The parents' role is to keep the arrangement squarely on course, to be helpful without enabling things to get worse.

When young adults encounter serious mental or physical health problems and need parental help, they still need a structured, clear agreement with their parents or caregivers for that support. Without discussing a plan or an arrangement, young adults will move back to their parents' homes and wait to feel good enough to move forward. But how likely is it that someone like Elena, Jack, or Courtney will suddenly feel the impulse to go look for a part-time job? Rules will help create momentum to move them forward when they cannot move themselves.

All supported young adults need to understand what type of support they are offered and under which circumstances. They need to know what they are getting, and what they are expected to give back, and they need it spelled out explicitly so everyone understands clearly. Young adults with health troubles need these kinds of agreements the most. Without the push of expectations, why would Jack make any sort of future for himself at all? He is facing a life of chronic illness, and it probably feels unfair and overwhelming. Do you think he's going to go out and apply for a menial job anytime soon? And consider Courtney, who has just recently gotten clean and sober. She is probably feeling overwhelmed by the daunting task of staying sober each day. Is she likely to be chomping at the bit to go take on the adult world? Or is she more likely to feel afraid, and retreat into the safety of allowing others to take care of her for as long as they are willing? But if they don't attempt to move forward and function again soon, won't it get harder the longer they wait? Without functional rehabilitation built in, what lives will they have in a year, or five years?

Perhaps the contract for parental support will shift from "I will pay for college as long as you make B's or above," to "You can stay with me as long as you see your therapist twice a week and attend AA or NA meetings regularly." If you're the parent, you may or may not feel she will be ready to find a part-time job soon. If so, you might add parameters for applying for jobs. Either way, there is still a need to clarify how you are helping, and what expectations come along with your support.

Even when they are seriously ill, supported young adults need to know what the plan will be and what they are expected to do to comply with it. Rules help them re-group. Giving them parameters helps them start moving again, even when they stopped moving because of a sickness. And while parents may worry that creating the plan for support could push a young adult like Elena to the brink, it need not be a harsh or even stressful set of expectations in order to provide the necessary scaffolding for her recovery. The plan does need to expect her to try to live again, but it doesn't have to hit her with a hard shove. Gentle expectations are often sufficient. Without enforcing expectations, the family may contribute to deeper levels of depression and shame, evoked by Elena's inability to overcome her fears and insecurities. When she doesn't do anything productive or progress toward any kind of goal, she won't like herself or her life very much. Not only is making a structured plan a safe move for a parent, it's an important aspect of being a member of the recovery team.

Young adults with problems can move toward health, and parents need to expect, or even require, that they attempt to do so in exchange for parental support. Without parental structure and expectations, the financial support or move back home can lead to young adults giving up on adulthood all together and ultimately getting worse.

CHAPTER 15

My House, My Money, My Rules

Consider Simone's sickness, and her parents' role. By the time a child reaches twenty, most parents consider themselves experts. Simone's parents felt secure in their parenting knowledge. They had always pushed her to work hard in school, follow the family's core values, and strive forward. Simone did all of these and more. She was responsible, kind, mature, and likable. She went off to start a young adult life her family was sure to feel proud of. The crisis that disrupted her new adult life was precipitated by Obsessive Compulsive Disorder (OCD).

Simone was always a bit high strung, but two years into her foray out away from the family, she was washing her hands fifty times every day and checking the locks so many times she often didn't leave for work until two hours past the start time. Her parents moved her home for treatment, and they started out with absolutely no worries about helping her. She had always been their cooperative, pleasant child. They never even discussed the need for rules when she returned home for treatment. It seemed self evident that she would comply with their wishes as she always had done.

Simone moved back to her parents' house, and her sickness was more pervasive than they had anticipated. Her OCD rituals were constant. If she couldn't clean or check things as her compulsions commanded, she became irrationally upset. Simone's problems quickly took over the entire lives of everyone in the household. She ordered her parents to disinfect every inch of the house to rid the place of germs. She invaded her parents' bedroom for access to the master bath to clean their bathroom or borrow soaps and sprays to shower and groom with dozens of times per day. In the kitchen, she bleached countertops hourly, and tossed out food from the refrigerator if it was more than a week old.

Her behavior was frustrating, but her parents knew that she was ill and needed to get well. They knew they had to let her get the help she needed, even when improvements didn't come fast enough. Treatment seemed slow, and improvements minimal. In the mean time, OCD drove everything she did; it was her whole life. Every waking moment was taken up with her fear-based activities. She had no time for normalcy. She didn't even consider returning to adult life. She made her nest at home, cleaned, disinfected, reorganized, ordered the family to maintain the cleanliness of the house to her standards, and she refused to venture out for fear of contracting a serious disease.

At first, her parents expected treatment to take care of the problems they were seeing at home. They were hopeful, telling themselves to just give it time. Simone was obviously still suffering from the effects of OCD when she threw out perfectly good fruits and vegetables, and even when she refused to leave the house. She didn't intend to be so pushy or demanding; she was responding to her own distress. They vowed to be patient with her. But as time went on, Simone's parents started to feel like prisoners to her illness. Her problems dictated every aspect of their lives, from the shopping list to the daily schedule. They spent hours scrubbing the house for her and going out to purchase replacement food items she had tossed, or cleaning products she used up. It became overwhelming. And expensive. They wondered how to get their own lives back under control, but didn't want to push Simone into a crisis by requiring too much of her. Her family was caught between the loving impulse to be patient, and the self-preserving impulse to tell her to knock it off. They assumed at first that the right course of action was to do as she asked, not set rules to require her to stop her behaviors. But they would eventually learn that OCD required the same kinds of rules as another chronic sickness. Just like the young adults in the previous chapter, Simone needed to strive to get better, not ease her efforts and give over to the sickness. Leaving her to fester wasn't going to be helpful. But initially her parents couldn't see that holding her to a standard of self-control was both doable and helpful.

They knew Simone was sick. She had OCD. She couldn't control herself, they reasoned. Their guilt clouded their ability to see that allowing Simone, sick or not, to give in the pressures of her disorder and take the whole family with her for the ride was making things worse. Rather than coming home to get better, she had returned home and gotten worse.

Simone's parents showed up in my clinic with Simone in tow, seeking consultation. They requested a change in her prescription medication, believing that biology in her brain explained the chaos in their household. On that first consultation, we spent a long time talking about psychotherapy techniques that tend to work best for people with OCD: namely, Exposure and Response Prevention (ERP). ERP encourages people with OCD to resist their compulsive urges and sit with their discomfort instead. Resisting action helps aid recovery from the disorder.

Registering what I was recommending, Simone's mother gasped, stunned. "She can control it?" she asked.

I responded, "Controlling it takes a lot of effort, and it's not an easy thing to do, but she can learn to control it to a degree, yes. And controlling her impulses will help her improve, along with taking medications."

I watched the information sink in. It was clear that in their concern and compassion, Simone's parents simply hadn't thought they could ask her to knock it off and stop the compulsive behavior. They didn't want to make rules and try to force her to control herself if it was impossible to control.

I wondered, what if Simone had struggled with addiction to drugs? Would it have been self evident to her parents that, although she was an addict, it would be okay to have a strict "no substance use" rule in the house? What if her problem was anxiety and avoidance? Would it be harder to make a "no avoidance rule" versus a "no substance rule?"

When a psychiatric diagnosis (or a medical diagnosis, for that matter) is a major reason for the move home, parents can become very uncertain about setting rules. My advice on this is very clear and consistent for parents with an adult child living at home for any reason: make rules. You'll definitely need rules. Don't feel guilty about the rules, either. Rules are a normal part of life; they exist everywhere.

Having an adult child at home and setting rules is not just permitted, it's often a vital piece of the puzzle for the young adult to get healthy again. Parents unknowingly shield young adults from the consequences of their problems by paying the bills and cleaning up the messes. Rules and expectations from the family prevent shielding from every consequence, and thus making things worse. One of the major tasks of parents of a young adult who lives at home is setting the rules. In fact, making the rules may be the only meaningful task to do once your child becomes an adult, whether she is sick or well. Simone's parents didn't find it intuitive to set rules for a their daughter because of her sickness. And yet young adults need to know what deal they have struck with their parents by moving home, even Simone. Structure and rules help them strive forward.

Simone's parents had historically been confident and assertive people. They had no qualms about insisting she do her chores or come home by curfew. But telling her to stop letting her sickness take over their house, or drain their financial resources felt like a different matter. Was she really able to control her actions? If they demanded she rein in her behaviors, could Simone be pushed into crisis? It was hard for them to tell. The situation felt much different to them than setting curfew for a teenager.

I told them to place some rules on Simone: "This is our house, and you cannot run it. This is our money, and you aren't entitled to spend it freely. We have to make some rules while you are staying with us. Rules will make things better for all of us."

A little skeptical at first, they consulted with her therapist to discuss the advice. How fragile was Simone? Was it okay to order her to manage her behavior? They wanted to be supportive, to give her the time she needed to get better in treatment, but the money wasted on food that went into the garbage was a growing stressor on the household. And the strain of trying to keep the house clean enough for Simone to feel comfortable was taking a toll. They wanted to set some limits, but it seemed insurmountable. Would it even make a difference? Simone's therapist advised that her parents do whatever it might take to maintain normalcy and order in their own home. That included reducing the amount of waste from tossing out perfectly good food. She advised them to create some rules and let Simone know she couldn't run amok at their expense. Her only caveat was to keep the discussion calm and logical. Getting upset wouldn't help matters.

So Simone's parents sat her down and told her that her OCD was out of control, and they couldn't live with her illness controlling everything. They made a few rules: "Stop throwing away our food, don't expect others to keep things clean to your standards, respect our private spaces and stay out of our bedroom/bathroom, and buy the products you need with money from your savings account rather than take them from us." They explained that the new rules had been determined because they couldn't afford to be so wasteful, and they were unable to meet her standards of cleanliness. They also insisted that she get out of the house for at least an hour a day. Allowing her to hide at home felt like enabling her to stay sick, and so they wanted to ensure she was using the opportunity at home to move herself forward, not slide back. The conversation about new rules wasn't easy, but ultimately Simone understood. She could see how unhealthy it was to ask her parents to throw away food and constantly disinfect the house. And although she would still defend her cleanliness standards, she could accept that her parents didn't have to do things her way.

While it took time and effort, Simone complied with their rules, and something encouraging happened. By controlling her responses to compulsions in accordance with her parents' rules, she gained better mastery of her symptoms. She started to make progress where there had been none before. Resisting the impulse to clean helped her tolerate germs. Leaving the house for an hour every day got her away from her preoccupation with cleaning. Bit by bit she improved for the first time since she had moved home. Their rules had an incredible impact because Simone hadn't felt strong enough to manage her impulses for her own sake, but she was a good follower of rules. The house rules helped take the responsibility solely off her shoulders, and allowed Simone to let herself make behavior changes she had previously felt incapable of making for herself.

OCD is not the only illness that responds encouragingly to rules. Kids who return home with other problems such as depression, anxiety, or addiction need rules and structure just as Simone did. While helping to support an emerging adult child, a parent has the power and the responsibility to set the rules of that help. Parents define rules in a variety of ways, more than, "We can't let your illness run the house." In some cases parents need to set a timeframe for support, like three or six months, or decide they will be helping indefinitely. They may need to define what type of assistance they are giving. In what way will parents offer help? A place to stay? Transportation? Food? While there are no simple right or wrong answers to how parents would or should assist an adult child, spelling out the plan is vital. Placing rules around the arrangement sets young adults up for progress, while failing to set rules can enable inertia.

When there aren't clear rules, adult children come back home to hide in their sicknesses, or worse – they revert to adolescent behavior. Unfortunately, in both cases parents might then resort to their old habits of "parenting." "Parenting" means taking over, giving orders, handling problems, and being the locus of control. A parenting mindset leads to regression into childhood behavior for the emerging adult. Now Mom and Dad are running the show, and the adult child is simply along for the ride. Parents might even try to punish non-compliant adult children, for example grounding them. This rarely works. Treating your adult child like an adolescent is likely to reinforce the childish behavior and set him back. If he's trying to face his anxieties about the future and he's regressing into the role of a defiant teenager, he might lie to you about having put in an application for a job or gone to a therapy appointment. When the goal for the adult child is to get him healthy, "parenting" is not the best route.

Rather than parenting, I encourage parents to think of themselves as the landlord or the benefactor. This young adult has come to stay for a while, and the landlord/benefactor has agreed to share resources as an act of kindness, to help this young adult get back on his feet. A generous landlord/benefactor would necessarily need to spell out the terms and limitations of the arrangement, but would not micromanage her charge. Yes, there would be rules, but there would be no "parenting" per se.

Whether sick or not sick, young adults who live with parents need to understand the rules for the arrangement of living in their parent's home. There is always an arrangement. It's never clear without discussion. In their effort to help, parents want to share, but the arrangement has parameters. It's never an "anything goes" relationship.

When a young adult living at home says, "I'm an adult now, I can do whatever I want," parents do well to clarify the arrangement for staying in their home by saying, "Yes, you can do what you want, but you cannot necessarily do whatever you want in my house." This stands in contrast to the way parents often argue about healthy lifestyles, or push specific values: "Decent people get home before midnight!" Shifting the focus away from morality, while acknowledging that a young adult is technically able to do what he wants is a more successful conversation. But in my house, I set the rules. Parents have an absolute right to dictate what goes on inside their own homes, whether the rule is "no swearing" or "we lock the doors at midnight and everyone needs to be inside for the night at that time." When young adults move home, there must be house rules, and those rules need to be explicit. It just works out better that way. Rules are the best recovery tool parents can offer.

Likewise, rather than complaining about the importance of an education, or pointing to wasteful spending habits, parents can say, "Another failing semester isn't a good investment," or "I am unwilling to spend money to contribute to your music collection." In essence, parents say, "When it comes to the spending of my money, just like the daily running of my home, I am the one who decides." This position starkly contrasts to the ways parents manage spending with children and adolescents before they become adults. When kids are young, parents may say, "It's my job to provide for you." When they become adults, it's not the parents' job anymore, but parents may choose to help, with the restrictions of certain rules.

Whether sick or well, young adults who move back in with their parents fare better when given rules. My house, my money, my rules. House rules work much like other rules in the adult world. *The rent is due on the first of the month, and if it's more than five days late, there will be a ten percent additional late fee.* Young adults understand these types of rules, and if they spent any time living away from home, they have already grown accustomed to them. If they have no experience away from home, living with boundaries and rules will help prepare them for later.

And, of course, the additional reason parents need rules when their adult children come home is this: the parents need order in a time of dis-order. When adulthood falls apart and your child ends up back home, you're scared and stressed. Creating order helps everyone get a grip on the situation.

CHAPTER 16

You Do You

When Courtney initially moved back in with her dad, they engaged in constant power struggles. He fussed about her clothes, her friends, her favorite TV shows, and basically every choice she made. Wanting to help her grow toward a normal, healthy life and away from her opiate addiction, her father thought he needed to force her to be more like him. His life was stable and predictable, and he wanted his daughter to have the same kind of safe life he had built for himself. He thought her questionable-looking friends would get her back into drugs. He thought her music was dark and angry and would lead to depression and addiction relapse. He thought her clothes would prevent an employer from considering her for a decent job or upstanding people from befriending her. In essence, her father tried to protect her by controlling every decision Courtney made as if she were a seven-year-old girl. His controlling approach led to blow-ups. Courtney was insulted. She was hurt. Why was everything she enjoyed branded as miscreant culture? She was an eccentric person with unique tastes. Why was her father unable to accept her as she was? Courtney felt disrespected and even bullied by his brand of "help."

After several heated arguments about his attempts to control, her dad finally agreed to join an Al-Anon support group for parents of addicts. He began attending weekly meetings where he sat in a room with other parents of addicts and listened as they talked honestly about their experiences. And while the other parents were strictly prohibited from giving him "advice" about how to handle things with his daughter, they each spoke of their successes and failures with their own addict children. He gained new knowledge and strength from the Al-Anon meetings, where the parents in his weekly support group encouraged one another to "Let go and let God." Fellow Al-Anon attendees told him they had all been in the same spot, terrified of facing another relapse and trying to control every move a child made. They had tried to protect their children by using control, but they had learned that it was a mistake to be so overbearing with an adult daughter or son. The group encouraged him to trust his Higher Power rather than try to control everything himself, and eventually to try to learn to trust his daughter again. It took him a lot of effortful self-control and hard work, but he did in fact learn to let go, and eventually he stopped trying to force Courtney to live a life he understood. Instead he just let her live. He dealt with his personal discomfort over her music and clothing. Instead of acting on his emotions, he talked to his group about his urges to make Courtney like himself. He accepted that his need for control was and indication of his problem, not Courtney's.

After getting clean and sober, Courtney found a job as a waitress and started paying her dad rent. She accepted adult roles bit by bit, and as she did so, her dad, aided by his Al-Anon work, backed away from telling her what to do. When she was a teen, Courtney had always begged for permission to get a tattoo, and her dad had said,

"Absolutely not." But now that she was a responsible, working adult, her dad felt he could no longer object to her choices. She had a right to choose for herself, and he wasn't about to kick her out on the street for a tasteful little red heart permanently etched on her wrist. As long as she was taking responsibility and growing as a healthy adult, he learned to accept that she could decide for herself.

While parents have the right and responsibility to dictate the terms of use for their resources, by the time children have grown into adults, it is no longer their role to dictate how adult children should think, feel, or behave most of the time. In fact, over-controlling can be incredibly destructive. For adult children, parents begin to adopt a "you do you" stance. When adult children are not utilizing the parents' resources, parents leave them to make their own decisions.

"You do you" encourages autonomy and accountability. Parents allow young adults to make their own choices, and leave them to accept responsibility for any outcomes related to those choices. Instead of controlling or teaching every necessary lesson, parents now begin to say, "You are an adult, and you are expected to do your own thing." But then they add, "and you have to clean up your own messes if you make a bad choice. I won't rescue you from your mistakes."

Often, this shift is difficult for a parent. After spending two decades or more giving directions, moving to a philosophy of letting adult children run their own lives unsupervised can feel unnatural, or even frightening and dangerous. Will they be safe? Will they make the right choices? Are they ready? It can be tempting to step in as the more experienced adult and do for kids what they need to do for themselves. But letting go is a vital stage of the separation process in young adulthood. If we want young adults to become independent and responsible, they need opportunities to practice making decisions (and even mistakes) without parents looking over their shoulders. In fact, they need to make mistakes and learn from them.

"You do you" means you choose your own clothes, music, living space, friends, romantic partners, classes, and even jobs. You decide if you want to wash your car, or drive a dirty one. And then you live with embarrassment if nobody wants to ride with you in your filthy vehicle. You decide if you want to attend religious services. You decide if you want to move to a new city to start over. However, what "you do you" does not mean is that someone else will foot the bill or clean up the mess if your choices don't work out as planned. In fact, it specifically means that you're on your own to orchestrate your plans and see your choices through. With the freedom to make your own life choices comes the responsibility for those choices.

It also does not mean, "Do whatever you want to do in my house." Adult children are free to run their own lives, but parents aren't obliged to tolerate shenanigans all about their homesteads. And that's the beauty of the "you do you" stance. Adult children are truly free adults, able to make their own decisions at any time, but restricted just like the rest of adults when their choices impinge on the rights and freedoms and the property of others. "You do you, but not with my money." "You do you, but not in this house." "You do you, but leave me out of it."

Of course, the "you do you" philosophy assumes that the young adult is capable of making independent choices. It can be difficult for parents to determine what young adults are truly capable of doing. Parents see failures and serious mistakes, and worry that young adults are unable to step out into the world and make sound decisions for themselves. Still, most young adults are capable of a least a little autonomy. They know that they don't like broccoli, and they want to finally have the choice as an adult to reject it.

As a professional with years of experience working with young adults who fail to launch or bounce back home in a crisis, I can say this: Most parents are more worried than their situation warrants, and the parents can usually let go more than it feels safe to do. If the parent of a heroin addict can learn in Al-Anon to let go and let his child make decisions for herself, any parent can.

CHAPTER 17

Relinquishing Control

O ut of all the young adults who have landed back in their parents' homes, I have never seen one benefit from their parents' holding on to control. This has been true for kids who are sick with a physical or psychiatric illness, and equally true for those who are healthy. Control does not bring resolution; it only contributes to young people staying stuck. Sure, sometimes families have to intervene. Parents first have to pick up the broken pieces of their adult child's crumbling life, and help get them back on their feet. Some addicts need literal interventions in order to get them into treatment. Some people with mental illness need to be nudged to get help. All young adults at home need structure and rules as the tools to help them regroup following a crisis. All people can use a bit of feedback from their loved ones from time to time. But interventions and nudges and rules and feedback are different from control. Brief points of thoughtful involvement are necessary, but in between those brief points, it is vital to learn to let go.

Whether Suzie leaves college because she feels like she is at the wrong school, or Johnny doesn't know where to begin after high school and stays with his parents, or if Helen starts hearing voices, or Jeffrey breaks his back in a fall, coming home to controlling environments or over-parenting households won't be the answer. Every young adult needs to learn to be as independent as possible, and as responsible as she or he can. Adults are not younger kids, even when parents struggle to remember that fact.

Whenever possible, the best thing families can do for developing young adults is let go of control. If young adults are going to go out (or even if they are going to stay with the family for a long, long time) and lead healthy, independent, maybe even productive adult lives in the future, they will have to be the captains of their own excursions. No young person is going to thrive with a parent constantly trying to take the wheel from their hands.

Ideally, the process of letting go starts years in advance of their final independence. We let them go in small increments: into the care of trusted others, off to school, over to a friend's home, to a middle school dance, off behind the wheel of an automobile, out on a date with a love interest, and ultimately off into lives of their own. We learn that we have to trust them, and they learn they are worthy of our trust. We let them try, and sometimes fail, and that's how they become strong and vibrant.

It all makes sense when it goes smoothly as planned, when teenagers follow the rules, succeed at school, accept new levels of responsibility as they come up, and graciously step into adult roles incrementally. But when things go wrong, too often the parental impulse is to take over. Parents take back control. "Here, let me." "You're doing that wrong. Do this instead." "What were you thinking?" And then parents who take too much control away from grown kids wonder why their adult children don't act like adults at all. They ask why little Johnny and Suzie look to parents to solve all the problems, why they cannot accept responsibility for themselves. When parents control, grown kids resort to adolescent behavior.

Overprotecting or holding on too long won't help kids stuck at home to circle back and get better. In fact, holding on too tightly or controlling too many things will keep them stuck for sure. Adulthood is about learning skills. Being controlled won't get them prepared.

Letting go can be difficult for loving parents. Parents worry that young adult children won't be ready. We give advice. We hover. We criticize and control. Recently, a 29-year-old working adult man told me that his hundreds of miles away parents called him every weekend and told him how much money he needs to be putting into his retirement account out of his weekly paycheck. The purpose of his visit was to seek help because he keeps screwing up his life, making poor choices, getting fired from jobs. I don't think it's a coincidence that a man who isn't trusted to run his own life by his family feels incapable of running his own life, and that he keeps screwing up. He doesn't trust himself. Why would he? What messages are imbedded in his mind, affecting his sense of self-worth when his parents won't trust him to make basic life decisions? What life lessons has he been robbed of the opportunity to learn by parents who exert this level of control in his adult life?

Maybe you're not too worried about how much your son or daughter will be placing in savings at 29, but what else will you be inclined to criticize or control, and what are the repercussions of doing so? Even the most self-aware parents can struggle with letting children run their own lives without supervising. And how much more tempting is it when a child moves back home, especially after some sort of failure or crisis, for a parent to try to take over? If you let them try and they failed, it's natural to feel an impulse to take control. But undermining your child's confidence and interfering with opportunities to grow won't lead to a better life. Quite the opposite.

In the end, letting go of control is the entire premise of this book. Control lands young people in treatment they may not need. It is often the family's desire to control that sends them to the psychiatrist or the therapist in the first place. "What's wrong here?" the parent asks. "Can't you fix this?" Families take their young adults down a road of interventionism. They get advice. They get medical treatments. They get nudged and corrected. But what is too often ignored is the fact that the stage of life of young adulthood is complex, and sometimes the unexpected twists and turns eighteen-year-olds are taking are just normal variations of the learning process. Messing up is not a sickness, nor a sign of ineptitude.

Even sick people need autonomy. Even sick young adults need to become adults in whichever ways they are able. Young adults with limited abilities need to exercise whatever control, whatever skill they have. They may need control even more than their healthy peers. After all, can you imagine being stuck with your parents? Stuck a child, in perpetuity? If a child lands back at home, the best medicine a parent can offer is to learn to let go.

Even when your child is in the sick role for depression, addiction, or medical illness, it's important to treat him or her as an independent decision-maker. Parents set the rules, and enforce the rules, but also know that there is always much beyond your control.

CONCLUSIONS

I t has been hard to write a conclusions section for this book because the conclusions have been intentionally scattered throughout each chapter. Nevertheless, drawing all the advice together will be helpful to some readers. In a single sentence, this book can be summarized as follows: The goal of raising children is sending them into adulthood, so you have to ready them and send them out, even when they struggle with sickness.

Sending them into adulthood isn't easy anymore, though. The line that divides child from adult has not only moved, it has become a gradual fade instead of a clear demarcation. As a family, you are going to have to determine *your* definition of adulthood for your children, and decide upon the steps you'll take to get there. Since you're creating your own program, I suggest you put it all in writing so everyone understands now and in the future.

If you already missed the boat on planning for your children, and your child grew up without anything written out, you'll have nothing to do unless trouble occurs. However, if your son or daughter didn't reach adulthood smoothly, it's time to make that plan, even if you're late in doing so.

And if you are the person stuck in limbo between childhood and adulthood, struggling to shake off the identity of sickness and take on adult life, congratulations on reading this book in its entirety. You don't have to wait for your parents to take action. You can begin to create structure by devising steps for growth, and measures of accountability to keep you striving for them. Don't hide in your sickness. Start living again.

Don't let physical or mental sickness confuse you. Adulthood is achievable, even if it requires accommodations. Entering the stage of adulthood means taking responsibility, but it is never one-size-fits-all. Some grown-ups live with their parents, and some only work part-time. The measure of adulthood is personal accountability. Adults take care of their own business. That's your ultimate endpoint, whether you are the parent or the child in the arrangement.

Weigh the risks of letting someone you love stay in the sick role for long if they have a mental illness, chronic disease, or something hidden and hard to measure. Stepping out of normal functional roles can lead to avoidance and make things worse. Staying functional is the key to growing up, in particular in this era of overparenting and prolonged adolescence. Young adults are under-experienced in the best of circumstances.

Getting truly stuck from sickness requires enabling. Families regress into enabling by doing things for stuck adults that they could reasonably do for themselves. The way out is to let go. Let each adult make choices, and then take responsibility when those choices turn out well or not so well. Let them learn through experience, as generations before them did.

But let's keep the emerging adult stage. It really is a beautiful thing to allow our kids more practice before they take on all the responsibility. And while we still need to iron out the kinks in the process of raising emerging adults, especially when things don't go smoothly, I'm hopeful that our society will figure it out. Until then, each household will have to write its own script.

ACKNOWLEDGEMENTS

I would like to thank the ladies of my former writing circle, now disbanded but forever in my heart: Linda Harris, Lea Glisson, Kathi Kardon, Becky McCarty, Janet Oglethorpe, Mercedes Stainken, Kara McGinnis, Mary Beth Edgerton and Tyra Manning.

I would like to thank all my friends and colleagues who served as beta readers, gave sage advice, and otherwise cheered me forward with this project: Darrell Smith, Shay Murphy, Shelley Allman, Audra Ochsner, Chris Ticknor, Madeleine Reichert, Sharon Lane, Ellie Brett, Paula Loring, and Sandy Deuter.

Special thanks to Dr. Jamie Daniel and Dr. Poonam Sharma for mentoring me through the world of publishing books.

Thank you to my editor, Jan Baumer.

A very special thank you to all of my patients and patient families past and present. You enrich my life by trusting me with your mental health.

Thank you to all of my staff, past and present, both in private practice and at Sigma Mental Health Urgent Care. You all inspire me to be better every day.

And, from the bottom of my heart, thank you to my home tribe: Brian, Chris, Zach, and Mia. Thanks for putting up with me while I've been on the journey of crafting this book. Thanks for bringing me coffee and nudging me forward. You guys are amazing!

CPSIA information can be obtained
at www.ICGtesting.com
Printed in the USA
LVHW050801060121
675395LV00006B/637

9 781937 985769